VALVE

A Literary Journal

FREIGHT
BOOKS

A CIP catalogue reference for this book is available from the British Library

ISBN 978 0 9566135 3 0

Designed and typeset by Freight

Freight Books
49-53 Virginia St
Glasgow
G1 ITS
www.freightbooks.co.uk

Editor
Catherine Baird

Deputy Editor
Craig Lamont

Fiction
Gabriella Bennett
Samuel Best
Matthew Lynas
Libby McInnes
Cameron Steel

Non-Fiction
Louise-Anne Geddes
Lauren Deegan
Debi Drysdale
Marianne Gallagher
Julie Shennan

Poetry
Martin Schauss
Richard Hampton
Katrina Patrick

Funding & Publicity
Lesley McKeran
Laura Blackhurst
Fraser Bruce
Simon Cassidy
Charlene Moore

Art & Design
Stewart Brower
Lynsey Cameron
Kathy Kunz

IT
Chris Beattie

The One Thing We've Got More Of

An Introduction to Valve Alan Bissett

Wither Scottish literature? Thirty years after the publication of Alasdair Gray's *Lanark*, which began a renaissance in our literary imagination, and seventeen years after Irvine Welsh and James Kelman carved globally-recognised classics out of Scotland's living language, what is our condition? To be sure, times are hard. A monopolised High Street bookselling industry, whose stock is controlled from the South of England, seems only able to recognise our novelists if they are writing in highly-commodified, easily-marketable genres. Scottish literature, as we once knew it, is unfashionable even within Scotland.

Oh, what a glorious opportunity.

Scottish writers work best when the odds are stacked against them. *The Year of Open Doors* anthology, edited by Rodge Glass in 2010, contextualised a hungry, new generation. At the launch for this book, I was able, for the first time in a long time, to look round and see predominantly young faces on the scene. There has, concurrently, been an explosion in literary 'performance' events which relentlessly cross-fertilise with music, film, theatre, comedy and live art: Discombobulate, Initial Itch, Monosyllabic, The Golden Hour, Words Per Minute and Neu Reekie!, to name but a few. There has been a rise in the once-moribund form of the literary journal, *Gutter* and *Fractured West* chief among them. Literary salons, where writers can connect with other writers, have sprung up in Glasgow, Edinburgh, Inverness, and even Lewis. A publishing company run on a shoestring by young people, Cargo, has appeared from nowhere, overflowing with ideas and enthusiasm.

This has all been done with a crucial absence of one thing: profit motive. While costs will always have to be covered, surrendering art entirely to the demands of the marketplace distorts and cheapens something we do simply to keep alive our souls, both individual and collective. Profit motive is what got us into this mess in the first place. It is the enemy of empathy.

The arts scene in Glasgow is one of the most vibrant in Europe and cannot be killed. Just as our youth has become politicised overnight by a savage assault on living standards and public provision, from a government in thrall to the financial sector, so too are our new writers making themselves heard. This journal exists, willed into being by students who simply ask that their voices, their individual selves, be recognised.

Presented here is a fresh selection of writers who are pursuing their right to be. In time, they'll inspire writers younger than themselves to take on a similar mantle, who'll simply think: if they can do it, so can we. *Valve* is a welcome new space for those who desire to wield language and imagination with an ever-greater dexterity, to test the power of their voices, their vision, to be afforded the chance to control their own imaginative universe.

We are cleverer and brighter than those who attempt to cow us into passive servitude or unthinking consumption. Journals such as *Valve* are how we will thrive. As St Jarvis Cocker once sang, 'We won't use guns, we won't use bombs / We'll use the one thing we've got more of, that's our minds.'

Contents

'It will take hours to marvel at all the gallery's exhibits but weeks to absorb their powerful message.'

Martin Schauss

Moth Journeys
Gabriella Bennett

———

Have you ever looked closely at a moth? I mean really closely. If you hold a dead moth against a window in the daytime, its wings become tracing paper and they change the white sunlight into a mottled yellow. You can now see all the tiny filaments that make them up. The pattern on its wings looks like a map of the world with all the countries it has been to. A fine layer of dust sits over a moth and leaves pollen-like stains on your hands that are difficult to get off if you're too rough with it. All the tiny hairs that protect its body look bristled by the light and sit around it like a protective shield of fur. Its curly tongue is a shock. You've never looked properly.

A moth starts its life as a grub, with a face that only a mother could love except it has no mother. It is helpless, a small white speck. Its mother attaches it near the things it needs: food, shelter, warmth. Then it leaves. It shortly becomes a caterpillar in an embarrassing stripy suit. Don't judge it, it doesn't dress itself. It is voraciously hungry – you've read the book. It turns leaves into ghosts of themselves. It walks comically – a sort of lurching gait on chubby legs. Then, when it is a little older, things slow down. It spends longer sleeping. It eats far less, newly conscious of its appearance. Everything looks like an effort as it begins getting ready to become a moth. It is quiet and introverted in its pupa, thinking and growing and constantly evolving. If the moth is disturbed in this state, it will wriggle and complain and make noises to warn predators away. It is not sociable. Eventually, the adult moth emerges. Its wings are soft and easily damaged so at first it keeps out of trouble until they harden and it can withstand knocks. Its whole being is fragile and scares easily at loud noises or unexpected happenings.

Have you ever wondered what being abandoned as a larva must do to a moth? It is entirely alone, pinned to the underside of a leaf after its mother dies. It never gets over such an early loss in its life. A moth would love to talk to a bird or a spider but it lacks confidence. It wants to go for a sugar water with a bee but it wouldn't know what to say. It prefers to be alone, and not draw attention to itself in case someone gets too close and sees the cobweb-thin beauty of its wings when they vibrate nervously in the dusk. A moth finds it difficult to settle down – there is an art to commitment that it cannot quite get to grips with. It flits from place to place without making a home for long period of time because no-one has ever shown it how to build lasting things.

Moths are not meant to be seen in the light. They are not made to give away their secrets freely. It is a lie that moths gravitate towards light-bulbs. Imagine you were living quietly in a dark place, feeling your way around things. No-one knows your history or what happened to your parents or how you arrived here or where you lived before. Then a light is turned on and you become temporarily insane with it. It is terrifying and lovely in equal measure; you absorb the colours you've spent time forgetting, each one screams suddenly out of the dark to you and lures you in. You blink your wings wildly to protect yourself and your head rushes with the effort so that you feel like you might pass out. You may fly at the bulb, but when it's off again you don't remember because it all happened so fast. Back in the dark your heart beats so fast it sounds like a low pitched buzz and sets the air around you alight with the noise. It takes a long time to forget the light bulb. You have nightmares about it – the feeling of the delicate fibres on your feet burning underneath you as you dance with terror. Sometimes it is easier to live in the dark.

A moth's wings are like two fingerprints – each pattern is completely different in some small way from another moth's. Spread, they can look like an owl's eyes in a layer of leaves, or camouflage completely into a brick wall. It is the master of disguise – it can adapt itself to fit any social situation. And like everybody else, it wants to be liked. A dead moth's wings can be pulled out gently to see what it looked like when it was alive. They look odd and dull though, like musty curtains that haven't been opened in a long time. In death, stretched and pinned to a white sheet in a collection, a moth exposes what it has spent its whole life trying to keep to itself. Only in pitch black flight can the true nature of a moth be seen as it flies invisibly through the air from its past.

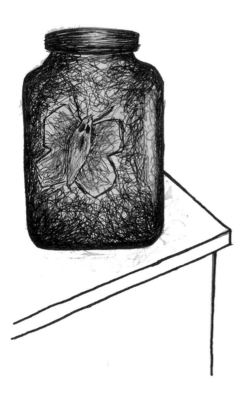

Snare
Catherine Baird

———

It's against the law. It's indiscriminate. You might trap something that takes ages to die. All of that courses through his mind as he ties the snare to the fence. Feed the kids, that's all. Can't live like this, can I? The snare is twisted wire, from a cable he stripped in the shed, the thin strands pleated and crimped to fashion a circle. The fence twangs, that strung out boing that brings him back to his days crossing fields in the early mornings with his granddad, the old man with his gun slung up over his shoulder in a long greasy canvas bag.

The feeling of pride when they brought back the catch. Gran's face when she opened the door. Once they had a partridge and two rabbits and she clapped her hands, then Granddad pulled a brace of duck out from the huge pocket stitched across the back of his shooting jacket. Her smile, the way she rubbed his cheek. He wanted to stand there forever. Michael's mouth had watered at the thought of the stews, the sweet carrot and onion and the thick gravy. Rabbit soup, his favourite - always with leeks, which he removed and strung along the flat rim of the plate like tickets.

The delight on Kathy's face if he brings something back, if he provides. He connects to that feeling as he strings the snare on the fence. He is sick of making do, of watching the kids eat chips and cheap burgers or fish fingers because he has no job. Kathy thinks it will be hard to get the kids to eat what he catches anyway, but Michael is willing to try.

Granddad showed him how to see the trail of the rabbit, what to look for and how to determine what was a fresh track or an old one. He showed him the bent grass, the run, the places where rabbits slip under fences and where a snare is best placed. Those traces of the past are what he uses to make his snare and position it. He walks the glen for hours, spying trails leading away from rabbit warrens where the animals come out in their droves. Granddad told him the best way was to snare one going back in; one that was scared or in a hurry and less likely to sniff out danger in its rush to get home. Michael ties the snare to a fence that runs between the old railway and the hill where the kids go sledging in winter. He secures it and tests how quickly it closes, tightening it around his wrist with a sharp tug. It nips his skin and there is a rush of remorse for what is to come.

Before the dawn breaks, Michael slips out of the house. He has slept fitfully, worried he would oversleep, and hopes that if anything is snared, it is dead already. He looks at the church clock as he passes: ten past five. The boys that had been kept on would be turning over for the last hour before getting up for their shift.

He walks to the main road then climbs up a steep incline to the cycle path. The railway has long gone, but the new path links the five villages where the trains used to pass. The path is usually busy with cyclists and walkers, berry pickers in the autumn, but quiet in the pre-dawn gloom. He walks along the grass embankment, to keep the sound of his steps from carrying.

Reaching the fence, he thinks his hands will shake, thinks he will have a dry mouth and a racing heart, but in truth, he expects there to be nothing in the snare. He steps up to the spot and reaches to pull back the long grass he had brushed back over his trap. He feels something warm and furry. The hands, mouth, and heart all happen at once and he lurches back. He listens for movement, but the animal doesn't stir. Reaching into the grass, he feels a hard paw and lifts the animal up to see what he has caught.

A hare, a fucking hare, he laughs, a fucking big hare.

He releases the noose from its neck, the fur caught in the snare's twists pulls away with the wire and the body flops over his hand. The warmth of it is surprising. When he had gone out with Granddad, anything they caught was cool and starting to harden, making for an odd, stiff feeling in the bag when he carried it home. This hare is long and supple and he curls it up, stuffing it into one of the kids' old school bags, long out of fashion.

He would let it hang for a few more days, but Kathy is adamant that the kids shouldn't see it. It swings from a coat hook in the cupboard by the back door, the head hanging back and the ears brushing the floor, and Kathy says there is a definite smell.

When they go to school, he promises, I'll clean it out on the back patio.

Michael prepares the area with newspaper to catch the skin and blood. He pulls out a tool bench from the hut, puts more newspaper on the bench and weights the corners with a spanner and some stones. Lifting the hare from its peg, he carries it out, past Kathy who grimaces.

Just wait, he says, you'd pay a fortune for this in a fancy eatery.

He lays the animal on its side on the bench. The blunt axe that he found in the shed is now sharpened and catches the sun as he raises it. It comes down with a thud that brings Kathy to the back door. Michael holds out the hare's foot to her, Good luck eh? She slams the door and he laughs. He brings the axe down three more times. Good luck. Good luck. Good luck. Blood drips onto the paper and the tail comes off next, falling like a dropped toy.

He cannot remember exactly how his granddad got the skinning started, but remembers him pulling the fur in one motion towards the head, chopping the head off from under the pelt. He calls Kathy to hand him a pair of scissors. She puts them out onto the kitchen windowsill and says she doesn't want them back when he is finished.

He snips the fur from the hare's back end and grips the skin. Lifting the animal to chest height, he pulls the coat in one long motion off of the dead beast. He cannot describe the sound. A sound that says an animal is being skinned that my children can eat; an animal is being skinned in one long tearing, stretching pull; an animal is being skinned and now it is meat. He lays it on the bench. The back is food and the front is the face and long delicate ears of a hare, brown-grey, like felt, and like life. He raises the axe and cuts the head off in a great rush. The skin and head fall to the ground, a teddy with no stuffing. He kicks it under the bench.

_'He lays the hare on the bench, its shape
like a greyhound on the run.'_

Michael knows what he has to do next – he must clean out the innards: guts, stomach, organs. He knows, but he remembers the smell, the sweetness, cloying forever in some cavity in his brain. He runs the edge of the axe along the length of the hare's underside, holds his breath and prizes open the body. He has closed his mind to the smell, but he cannot avoid the sight. The yellow red orange green black purple of it, slopping in curls of intestines, sacs of matter, black gobs of blood; a horror story in his hands.

Holding the animal by its back, he shakes the innards to the ground. Folds of colour hang from the beast and pool on the newspaper. Strings of fat and corded veins attach them to the skinned form and Michael pushes his hand into the chest cavity and scrapes the offal out, tugging pieces of sinew and gristle away from the cleaned meat.

He lays the hare on the bench, its shape like a greyhound on the run. He lifts the bench aside and rolls up the newspaper on the ground, making sure all of the offending waste is enclosed. He feels the give in it as he places it in the bin, the contents rolling and squirming.

He turns on the hose and lets cold water run over the hare and his hands, then the axe and the scissors. As the water trickles to the drain he sees a piece of meat on the ground. He picks it up and it is the heart. It is small and firm and Michael pictures it pulsing, pumping; its rapid beat forcing blood and energy and oxygen to the hare's muscles as it ran free.

Babbity Bowster
Martin Schauss

———

Bring the beer back from the brewery and break the brass barrel
Bear the beer and the bore in the bar
Bark at the barman for the booze is bad
Beat the beat on the breakdance base and brag to the bare babe in boots
Better back off from the bare bitch that brings her big brown bear
Broken bones after the brown bear bragged his biceps, like bricks on butter
Bring better beer, bring broader, till broad bewilderment becalms

The Harmonica
Martin Schauss

———

It is a Hohner Marine Band, a diatonic pocket harmonica, ten blowholes, twenty notes, C Harp – blues. Its cover is nickel-plated, coating the wooden body and its reed plates. Hold it in your hand and feel how light this simple instrument is. Follow the old harpdog's tale and dunk it in a glass of whiskey or vodka before you break it in if you want it to be louder. Refrain from baptising the harp if you want its life expectancy to be greater. Break it in gently, remember it's the first time. Keep your teeth slightly parted, mouth and jaw relaxed, lips moist. Breathe from the diaphragm. Blow softly; draw even softer. Be patient, it will sound out of tune at first.

Once you've broken in your harp, you can exploit it more fully. You can now start tonguing. Touch the tip of your tongue to the roof of your mouth just behind the front teeth, then drop the tongue and exhale. Curl and uncurl your left hand around the harmonica like a tent to let the sounds vibrate. Try vibrato on long sustained notes. Once you succeed in using these techniques on your melodies, you can try bending notes. This might appear tricky at first and there is no one way to explain it. Everyone will experience their first bending differently. But it is often described as drawing in whilst whistling. Or pretending to drink from a straw that goes directly to the base of your stomach, sucking in the air rather than simply breathing. The important thing is to practice hard. Your harmonica will seem reluctant at first, but it will soon give in. Some blowholes are easier to bend than others, too. Try them out.

If you have not played your harp for a while or had it in your pocket, slap it against the palm of your hand a few times before use. This will dislodge fluff and dust between the reeds and you can just blow them out. And always remember to rinse your mouth before you play.

The Story of How a Young Cliff Parkshaw Brought Down Charlie 'The Bear' Watson

Matthew Lynas

——

Well please if you've got the time let me tell ya somethin darlin. Let me tell ya somethin about what it feels like to stand on a fence and shout 'by nelly this is my home'. Let me tell ya a story about what it was to know patience, if you've got the time. There aint no body it seems that's got time for an old raconteur like me. So they say anyway. I don't know who they are any more but that's for another yarn. I guess they used to be us. Then who am I now? Ah whooey let's not get into all that. Sit yourself down and turn off that rackety humming whizzing brain of yours.

It was summer in 1953, I was out working in the baking heat on my Daddy's farm. It wasn't the biggest farm you ever seen, just a couple of fields a few miles south-west of Richmond. Fixing my bootlaces I had cause to stop for a moment and stare down at the yellow way the grass had turned in the dry heat. The grass wasn't long cut for the making of hay you see. Well those soft green blades had been turned to bristles. It was like the ground had a six o'clock shadow. Everything changes with the seasons, it's just a matter of what calendar you keep. I remember hearing horses in the trees. I lifted my head catching something in the air. On a hot day you would swear you could smell tobacco in every corner of Virginia.

'Hey boy what do you think you're doing here? We told your Pop this is gona be our land. Why don't you run on home and pack some boxes?' Three men on horses had came out of the tree line that marks the end of our plot and the start of one of the many, many, many farms that had been bought up by the big tobacco companies. Now you might be fixing to know why these boys were ridin horses. Well this aint New York City we're talking about here, you won't find no Manhattan beatniks coursin through our fields in some open top hotrod. What you have to understand is that the countryside doesn't move through time like the city does. That aint to say it moves slower, just more deliberate.

'Cliff? Ah said Cliff boy are you listenin to me? Go run tell your Daddy that if he don't sell up tomorrow we're gona torch that house o' yours ya hear?' I was staring up at the leader of the three. His horse was just a touch taller and he was wearing new denims on his legs, his arms were thick like the branch of a Yellowstone tree, one of them huge redwoods that they build tunnels through. They called him The Bear when he went drinking with his buddies. Old Mrs Watson, his mother, called him little Charlie. He used to have a farm, now he was an enforcer for some tobacco company or other. Didn't much matter which one, whoever was paying I guess.

'We aint selling Mr Charles,' I said, my poor old brown coated bitch Sally run across the field down beside me, growling from my knee up at the horses. I clenched my fists hard in my pockets. 'This is our fields do you hear? Now why don't you just run along and tell your bosses that the Parkshaws aint for moving. They too much like being their own damn bosses than listen to some Richmond suit.'

Now Charlie The Bear didn't like being talked to in such a way, especially not by some fifteen year old hick. He jumped down from that horse of his and walked right over to me while his two lieutenants jeered from their horses. One had patchy blonde hair that sprouted out his head at all angles; the other was a round little fella with a military crew cut. Now Sally pushed against my legs and looked up at me more than once. The funny thing about courage is it aint got nothing to do with being afraid or not. If you aint afraid of jumping in a snake pit or climbing some cliff then my blessed you aint courageous, you're a damned idiot. Well I was pretty scared as I stood there waiting for Charlie. He was about three steps away when I lost my breathing, it just went on its own. In and out, in and out. You can't hide that sort of a thing and Charlie could see my chest puffing up to twice its normal size. I wouldn't say I was crying, but I wanted to. Oh did my eyes begin to sting.

'Now you listen to me. You're lucky you're a kid or I'd tear a smile all around your face with this here hunting knife.' Charlie pulled a nine inch blade from his belt. It didn't shine under the bright Virginia sun, it was too coated with dirt and who knows what else. Sweat started to drip from just under my eyebrows running down the side of my nose. Sally's throat was rumbling.

'Are you gona tell your Daddy to sell up? You better ask him, beg him to listen to me. Or I'm gona start cutting things up around here.' My right leg was twitching. I could feel it just around my knee. My face was about eye level with Charlie's chest. He stepped back enough that I could see his grin. He was looking back at me. Sally let out a bark, I shook my head. 'We're gona burn that house of yours down then boy,' he said, then he swung that big leg of his at Sally's face.

Now most dogs, Virginia dogs, can take a kick or two. I aint saying it's right and I aint saying it was common practice on our farm but it happened. But the thing is Sally was an old bitch. Charlie was walking back to his horse with the slightest sign of a limp. He had caught Sally right in the skull, a little harder than he probably meant to if he didn't want to break a toe that day. I dropped down beside Sally but she wasn't moving. I felt her belly, right where I used to scratch it. There was nothing moving, nothing was churning or pumping or beating or thumping. She was perfectly still.

Charlie was mounting his horse when I ran after them. One of those two friends of his turned and laughed as he saw me try and chase down three men on horseback. I could see it was no use running so I stopped. Now I don't quite remember what I was thinking but in one last ditch attempt at stopping those three fellas I pulled my own little knife from my belt, the one I used for odd jobs around the farm. I held the dull blade, feeling the hot sun on my neck, and I threw it with all my strength.

The knife moved in an arc through the sky but it looked a mile off target. Or so I thought. But for some reason, and to this day I don't know why, but Charlie's horse stumbled and jerked to the left and that little hunting knife of mine caught it just under the thigh. The horse went down. It was the kind of dull thump that only comes from colliding nature, that sound don't exist in any steelworks. I turned away and ran back to the house as quick as I could. I didn't hear until later that the horse broke two legs on account of the strange angle of its falling. I didn't hear until later that when Charlie hit the ground he dislocated his shoulder and snapped his shin bone. Now I didn't see it but I can imagine the crunch, there weren't any soft autumn leaves under those trees, just dry Virginia dirt cooked as hard as concrete slabs broken apart by tree roots. On that summer day I dropped Charlie the Bear to the ground and I didn't even stick around to see it. I just ran as fast as I could back to my Daddy.

I should tell you that Sally didn't get back up and for two nights I cried before sleep. Like I said she was an old bitch and every old bitch drops some time but that don't change how you feel when it happens. I'd like to tell you that was the end of our troubles. I'd like to say that our little farm forever prospered and that no more enforcers came round our way. I wish I could tell you that they didn't stick a bullet in that poor horse or that we had no more trouble from the big tobacco companies. Most of all I wish I could say that to this day those fields are still under the care of the Parkshaw family. But I can't do that. All I can say to you is that there's less to be said for choosing your moment than knowing when the moment's chosen you.

On visiting a museum of modern art

Martin Schauss

——

For Christmas, Mary and Jack got from their daughter-in-law a year's pass to the newly erected modern art museum which now embellishes the historic city centre and strives to compete with museums all over the world, ablaze with light reflecting from their outhouse glass pyramid or shining in the sun by the riverside in random titanium curves, and the new museum, with its smart acronymic name, has its doors open 24/7 because this is the new thing and in the night a visit is particularly rewarding because the manifold colours of the neon lights, installed by this famous interior designer from France, echo through the exhibition halls as if their walls were made of mirrors, contrasting with the blackness of the night, let in by the expensive window ceiling, an architectural masterpiece by this celebrated Chinese-American architect who insisted so on his choice of material, and on the outside the spots enlighten the titanium and slate edifice, of which various parts are cloaked in carbon fibre and whose silver glow gives this magical mood and positively overwhelming eeriness when one's eyes defocus against the sleek silver façade, and it is this abstract structure which boasts some of the world's most cutting-edge exhibits, golden vases depicting bears being sodomised by Asian princesses, monochromatic canvases capturing the anxieties of modern societies, black and white videos of an Eastern bloc female raping herself and hammering nails through her brain, metallic constructs towering high in strange angles filling the room but not its walls, computerised installations shooting geometric patterns on screens with labels warning epileptics and expectant women, and it will take hours to marvel at all the gallery's exhibits but weeks to absorb their powerful message, but everyone knows it will have been worth it and the excellent experience is gained for life and culture and knowledge, and Mary and Jack will be eternally thankful to their daughter-in-law.

For Sale
Craig Lamont

———

The windows are blind, the front door locked for good. Grass on either side is a stubbly crew cut. Plants and weeds that march by the fence bend over crippled. The house is not an imposing structure. In its day the neighbours were shocked when they entered, in awe of how it seemed twice as big as it should be; so many doors in a hall like a heart connecting the rooms.

Severed from all this; a wooden shed of mismatching boards at the end of the back garden. It looks like it is waiting on you. The closer you get the more you see, the more you imagine inside. A lawnmower, an old bike. Shapes mingle as the sun peers through the boards. When you open the door you see a stack of browned envelopes. You pick them up and see Her Majesty's Seal, already broken. By the same hand the same address is scrawled and as you unfold the same hopeful words, you know you will not buy this house. As you leave you look up at the noise, a fighter jet, and wonder where it is going.

Summer Past
Libby McInnes

———

She rolls up slowly, riding the brake to a quiet stop.
Music lowered to silence, handbrake button pressed in a delicate upward pull.
Headlights beam on Violet, her first car.
A fine layer of dust has settled on her bonnet, like downy fuzz on a peach.
Veins of purple seep from the stagnant blanket, withered tracks where the window-washer ran.
The sticky residue of the 'L' plate still visible on the windscreen.
She remembers.
Foot stuck on the brake, scared to shatter slipping memories with movement.

Sunglasses and dripping pink and blue ice-cream unscrubbable from the two front seats.
Clapping and singing to songs she had never heard before and would never hear again.
Sand grains knitting themselves into the carpet, imprinted like the smell of Stella summer.
His eyes unblinking, hands cupping her cheeks.
Spacious back seats and exhaling as one, the blazing globe dipping into the sea.
The warmth of the darkness, one cardigan to cover them both.
Salted skin, soft under steady palms.
The belief in forever.

The Film

Chris Beattie

———

Black screen. In the distance, bells can be heard chiming. Fade in. Two silhouetted figures stand before a spring sunset. Pan out to a sea of spectators, sitting in a uniform pattern divided in the middle. They chatter excitedly at each other, but only the bells can be heard.

The final bell chimes, replaced with a rhythmic heartbeat. Cut to a point-of-view shot of a man walking up to the platform from behind, walking in sync with each thudding heartbeat. For the first time, we see clearly the two figures, perfectly framed against a backdrop of excited faces.

Close up of all three people on the platform, facing them straight on. On the left, a well dressed gentleman, gazing into the eyes of the woman on the right. She looks and – for the first time in her life – feels like a princess. Two steps behind them stands the only man who can change everything. And at last, we hear the very first words of the entire piece.

'We are gathered here today…'

INT. DOMINIC'S FLAT - DAY
Dear Dominic. We thank you for visiting us. We were impressed by your directorial ability, but unfortunately, we feel that you are perhaps too overqualified for our needs. We simply want a normal wedding video that we can look back on one day, and have opted to have our nephew Gary record the ceremony on his camcorder for free. We wish you the best of luck in the future. Sincerely, Adrian and Mary.

There really are some fucking philistines in this world.

They tell you this only once at film school. In the very first class, you are confronted with the archetypical Withnail, ending every sentence with a nihilistic sigh. He directed a few episodes of Emmerdale, back when it was Emmerdale Farm. You promise yourself that you will never turn out to be this person.

'Master your craft,' he says. 'And once you've mastered your craft, forget everything you ever knew about it. Because stereotypes, clichéd dialogue, toilet humour and happy endings are what the public think films are about. And the public don't ever want to be proved wrong.'

After that, it's all French arthouse, trips to the GFT, and obsessively reciting quotes from The Room. Conversations turned into contests, with the words 'I don't think I've actually heard of that director' indicating the immediate loser. At no point did we reconsider Withnail's whiskey-tainted warning. On average, the inciting incident of any film occurs within the first ten minutes. At this point in my life, twenty eight years is beginning to seem like a bit of a stretch.

INT. THE RUSTED CROW – EVENING

'How are the job prospects, then?' He said it into his pint glass, hoping to distance it from the same sort of tone my parents use when asking the same question.

'Fine.' I answered in exactly the same tone when responding to my parents.

'How did that wedding video thing go?'

'There were some... artistic differences Donald, I'll be honest.'

When I first moved in with Donald, he seemed like the ideal flatmate. He did three years of sound production, and had a passion for the art that didn't equate with his dribble of skills. In those three years, I'd never seen him happier than when he spent endless nights slapping halved watermelons into buckets of yoghurt, trying to find a perfect sound effect to use for an independent film. One year after graduation, he took up a job in an accountant's office, and hadn't committed any crimes against dairy since.

He's Peter O'Toole in Lawrence of Arabia: a battered shell of the enthusiastic young man he was when he began his journey. The only satisfaction he got from life these days was a little less artistic and a little more primal.

Amy-Louise was an actress. She joined a local youth drama group at nine years old, and remained there until the director had to admit that the appearance of a twenty-two year old orphan in their production of Annie was beginning to look a little incongruous. Her largest role to date was 'Impatient Queuing Lady #2' in an episode of Monarch of the Glen. She even stuck a hyphen between her first and middle name in the hope that it would give her more gravitas in casting sessions. So far, it had only worked on Donald.

'We could do another film,' I suggested.

'I don't see it,' replied Donald. 'We don't need another runner up prize at a student film festival.'

Amy-Louise giggled. 'Besides. Donald and I have already made enough films this month, isn't that right?'

Donald lowered his head, and a slight jolt in the way he was sitting suggested that he'd just kicked Amy-Louise under the table.

As I watched the two of them, I started grinning. Because Withnail was wrong. The public don't just want stereotypes, clichéd dialogue, toilet humour and happy endings.

They also want sex.

INT. VIDEO SHOP – DAY
Anyone looking at me at that point would've shaken their heads and told their children to 'stay away from the strange man.' And I'm sure I did look strange, as I took down notes on a fast food napkin while looking at the back of *One Came Over the Cocksucker's Chest*.

'Do you need a hand?' asked one of the staff members. It was the same one who had been ducking and swerving behind video racks for the past twenty minutes, trying to keep a covert eye on me.

'Yeah, actually. I'm looking for something that isn't as stylistically contrived. I don't want a deus ex machina appearing in the form of a plumber. I want drama and tension. Conflict. Tragedy. I want something that will open my mind as much as it opens my trouser zip.'

He frowned and folded his arms. 'What you want, sir, is a girlfriend.'

INT. THE FLAT – DAY
When Donald got home, he had to give the state of the living room a second look. Suspiciously labelled VHS boxes and blank tapes were strewn near the TV. I sat in front of it, legs crossed, like a child on a Saturday morning.

'Tell me that's not what I think it is,' he said. A very slight blush painted his cheeks. I didn't turn away from the screen. 'Research!'

'Whatever you're researching,' he said as he retreated to his room, 'I don't want to know.'

This was going to be more difficult than I realised.

INT. THE FLAT – NIGHT
I had to keep telling myself, 'This is the right thing to do.'

I could work on exposition later. I'd write a quick script and get Donald and Amy-

Louise to act out the main points of characterisation. They wouldn't bat an eyelid. They'd assume it was another one of my screen tests for a hazy idea that wouldn't make it out of pre-production.

It wasn't just about the money. I was desperate for cash, but this was something more important. It was about the art. I was bringing culture and integrity to the only genre of film which hadn't made the leap into respected cinema.

'This is definitely the right thing to do,' I told myself, as I installed the webcams into secreted areas of Donald's bedroom.

INT. THE FLAT – DAY
They weren't as harsh as they could have been. They could've gone to the police. It's not as if they didn't have any evidence.

I paid the last month of outstanding rent, and gave them half of the profits. Amy-Louise wanted all of it, but Donald settled on half. It was all done on the understanding that I'd take the video down as soon as possible, move out of their flat, and never speak to them again.

I don't think Donald will stick to that last condition. Sooner or later, he's going to remember why we became friends in the first place. He's going to miss those buckets of yoghurt one day, and when he does, he'll pick up the phone and ask if I fancy a drink.

I was already opening the door with my suitcase when he walked over with an envelope in his hand.

'Before you go, this came for you this morning,' he said, handing it over.

I took it, and slapped it across my palm, and sighed. 'End of an era, eh Donald?'

'Get the fuck out of my flat.'

The door slammed behind me, and I stood on the close landing for a few minutes, hoping the door might open again. It didn't. I picked up my suitcase, and made my way down the stairs.

EXT. OUTSIDE THE FLAT – DAY
Dear Dominic. It has been two months since our previous correspondence. Since then, we have come across one of your more recent works. While we are saddened that things didn't work out with our wedding video, we would like to ask for your services again. This time, it's for a video that would not be appropriate for Gary to record. Sincerely, Adrian and Mary.

A Portrait

Richard Hampton

——

A day tracker is six pounds on Sunday and we could go wherever we liked. I fancied Derry but it was too far away and you fancied Bangor but that was too close to home. We didn't meet half way; we got off at the second stop, which was Moira. We found a carryout and got some beers. We found a field with just two trees. It was acres big and flat and open with just two trees to sit under. They stood an age away from each other and seemed to be a reflection of themselves. We'd try out both. I tried to climb the first but felt a spider and jumped, so we nestled against its rough bark and limbish roots. You cracked your can; I followed your lead and drank deep. I smoked a cigarette to keep away the wasps and you checked your phone for something more important. I licked your face from chin to nostril because I knew I had bad breath. You laughed and squirmed and rubbed the wet on my cheek. A wasp was in my beer and I let out a cry and you laughed at me while I jumped like a child. We went to the next tree and I smoked again. It was just us, the grass and the two trees in this empty. You could paint a picture to mind the memory. The trees like us were far apart, but were closer together than anything else.

Memories with her

Richard Hampton

——

I didn't see my grandfather, it was too much. Auntie Eileen had always been dead, sat on her arm chair, blind from threading needles in the mill. Myself, my father, brother and a neighbour would visit her on Saturdays after the football. I can't remember what they talked about. My father would pour a tiny bit of beer into my Sprite because I pretended I liked shandies at that age. Come nine o'clock or whenever my father had finished his conversation can, we'd be ready to go home. My Auntie Eileen would point to the next room for our reward - one pound each. This doubled our pocket money. My father would collect the sandwiches she had made him. Always roast beef with an inch of margarine which my mother would scrape off to save the beef. A lot of things happened on those Saturday nights, winning the cup, winning the league, my father throwing my shoe in a field because I said he wouldn't. Covered in chalky makeup and a forced grin, lay those memories with her.

I wanted to punch him so I did

Cameron Steel

——

He was seven when his Dad first hit his Mum and fourteen when he first hit up; using the spoon he used to eat his cornflakes with. *Goat a fag? Goat a fag?* The clarion call. *I woulda boat some fags but a'hid tae buy some mulk fer the waen you know wit it's like.* Yes of course. He was dancing on the spot like a sparrow on a hot spoon. So I swung hard and fast. Landing on jagged cheek, he fell, crumpled. Sharp and skeletal, to the ground and lay like a pile of coat hangers. *Aaw whit ma nose man.* His girlfriend cradled him in her arms like that Bellany painting. *Wit ye daein ya prick- he's asthmatic- people like you shouldnae be allowed to walk the streets.*

Flight

Samuel Best

Excerpt from a novel.

———

'Here!'

A voice shouts across the pub and cuts Niall off. We all turn and look. Three guys, a bit older than us, are standing by the doorway. Three massive guys, blocking off the main exit.

'Here!' One of them shouts again, taking a step forward, 'Wan ae you boys pulled a blade on me last week.'

He reaches inside his jacket pocket and pulls out a small kitchen knife. Smiling, he turns it slowly in his hand.

'Well now it's ma turn.'

'Shit.' Jake says, looking round at us.

'None ae this pish in ma fuckin pub. The lot of yous, out. Polis are on their way.' The barman stands behind his taps, his chest puffed, eyes fixed. 'Fuckin move. Now.'

The group of lads look at the barman, the biggest one still turning the knife in his hand.

'Naw, we're no leavin. These dicks pulled a knife on me, an am no lettin them away wi it.'

Niall tries to calm the situation.

'Oh fuck off, mate, that wisnae us.'

'Aye, it wis. Lithgae Arms, the other week. I remember. Yous were wi some other dick wi a knife.' The guy replies, swaggering forward. 'So where is he now, eh? No got yer big mental pal tae protect ye?'

A couple try to move towards the doors but one of the other lads glares them back to their seats. Jake speaks up, his voice cracking at the start.

'Calm down, mate, that just all got out of hand. We didn't want any–'

'I ken ye didnae want any trouble, but yous fuckin started trouble. So belt it.'

Pete gets out of his chair and the guy holds the knife up towards him.

'Not one mere fuckin step.'

I look around for a door, a window, Christ, the hole in the wall this fucking pub is named after. There's a corridor leading to the back, but I don't know what's there. Maybe a door outside, maybe a cleaning cupboard. I can see the barman, still watching the group of lads, muscles tense. I turn back around, and see the other two guys have moved away from the door and towards Pete. Customers start running out behind them. Pete rests one hand on our table.

'Alright, calm down. I'm not going anywhere. Why don't we just think about this? The police will be here soon. If you leave now–'

'We're no leavin any time soon, pal.'

Pete's hand moves slightly. A twitch. Then another, more exaggerated this time. I stare at his hand, and look at Niall, then Luke. They follow my gaze.

'Well if you're here to stay, how about a wee drink?'

In a split second, Pete picks his empty pint glass off the table and hurls it towards the group. We don't hang about to see the result. We run, scattering our chairs across the pub, and head straight for that corridor, Pete leading. Behind us, I hear screams and footsteps on broken glass. Then, 'fuckin go after them!'.

Pete pushes a door open, and we're hit by the cold air of outside. We look around, trying to spot a way out to the High Street, to an alleyway, to fucking Neverland. Shouts from inside the pub keep us moving.

'Over the wall, quick!' Jake says, already starting towards it.

We start to climb, and I hear the door open behind us.

'They're off over that fuckin wall!'

Turning, I see two guys, the ones without the knife, run towards us, hands scratching for grip on the old stones. I clamber over the top of the wall, and drop down into the bushes below. Pete and Jake are already there, catching their breath, and Niall follows seconds after me.

'Where now?' I ask.

Peter squints into the darkness, panting heavily.

'This way.' He takes off at a run.

We continue through the bushes, skin scratched by thorns and branches, and it gets darker and darker the more we run. Before long we come to another wall, smaller this time, but it's hard to really tell from looking. I'm squinting so hard my eyes hurt, and my skin stings from tiny cuts. We scale the wall and gather on the other side.

'Where are we?' I ask, looking around. There's a set of grassy steps leading up to something I can't see, and a path leading one way to streetlights and another to thicker darkness.

'Fuck that - where are they?' Niall says, spitting on the ground.

We stand still and listen.

Nothing.

Nothing but our lungs filling, coughing, emptying, and the occasional branch snapping in the distance.

Jake whispers, 'They must be lost in there.'

'Is there another way out?' I ask.

Pete shakes his head. 'That's the old arcade down the other way. They'd need to break in. Here...'

He points to our left, down the path leading to street lights.

'What do you think, onto the High Street, or through the Peel?'

'Peel, definitely. It's pitch black, and fucking massive. They'll never find us.'

We nod at Jake and continue along the path, half walking, half jogging. Our lungs burning, stomachs full of acid. The Peel is a big park, with Linlithgow Palace sitting at the top. Roofless and desolate, you'd half-expect Béla Lugosi inside, and yet we start towards it across the space once flooded for protection.

'Fuckin hell, man.' Niall keeps saying, still trying to spit the taste of exercise out of his mouth.

We reach the top of the Peel, by the Palace, and stop for a moment. Listening again, there's just the gentle lap of wind blowing waves across the Loch. No footsteps, no shouts. It's just us and the breeze.

'Y'hink we're awright now?' asks Niall.

'Dunno.' Jake replies, squinting down a road leading back to the High Street.

'Wait,' he says, narrowing his eyes further, 'No. Look.'

Three figures walking up the road, near indistinguishable in the shadows, stop. After a second, they burst into a run. We turn quickly and head down the other side of the hill. Stumbling and slipping down the grassy slope, we eventually reach another path. It winds through an old gateway and alongside the Loch. Sleeping birds, awoken by our noise, squawk and fly in a cloud of confusion across the path. There's shit everywhere and my feet skid with every step. I look behind and see the three guys gaining speed. My feet skid again, and I feel my knees twist and buckle. One foot leaves the ground. No purchase, it cuts through the air in an upwards arc. The other follows. My arms reach out for something, anything. A branch. My fingers close around it, rough and cold on my skin.

Crack.

It snaps free, and my whole weight comes down on the concrete. With a dull thump I land on my hip.

'Fucking–'

I scramble up and try to run again. My left leg feels slow, as if the drinks earlier have focused on those muscles, weakening and loosening them until they can barely work. I struggle on, hip aching, clothes and hands slimy with excrement.

We cut through the Vennel flats and reach the road. We weave through a line of traffic and onto the opposite pavement. The three guys are still coming, having reached where I fell, but not succumbing to the shit slide of a path. Niall turns to us.

'Look, get on.'

We follow his gaze up the road. A small bus is making its way closer and closer to us. The front is poorly lit but we can just make out the info.

38
Falkirk Bus Station

Four hands get stuck out into the road and the bus indicates left. We get on and the driver gives us a withering look.

'Four singles. Falkirk. Change is yours.' I say as Jake, Pete and Niall head for seats near the back. I hand the driver a tenner and the doors hiss shut.

Blue Dot
Catherine Baird

| Light on the air like dandelion seed
a drone overhead takes reams of film
noting changes in loess ledges
or new square tin structures blotting landscapes
shapes of missile silos
ice on rivers building bridges between disparate states
and icebergs yawing and splitting.
See our world from faraway
watch it flicker light and dark in its spin cycle
a yin yang miracle
see it humbled in the vastness of space
its drones pinpricks of vigilance for
the blue dot's panopticon
see it slow or stop
the sun expanding out to eat it up
like a storybook monster

Rules
Debi Drysdale

———

'When you have an eating disorder your voice is taken away,'
Natalia's words echo in my mind, stirring up memories that I'd hidden away. The reality of this statement is something I know only too well. I've seen the empty and exhausted eyes, the glazed expression and the frozen vocal chords. The way the choking rules take over, how they consume, how they control; they steal your voice, first. *It's the first major casualty in a war that takes no prisoners.*

Working as an Ambassador for B-EAT (The UK National Charity for Eating Disorders) Natalia Rose is a confident, independent and successful woman. She is completely in control of her life and raises awareness of eating disorders through the media, working to make it easier for sufferers to speak up by removing stigmas and offering practical support. Looking at her now you would never know the harsh truth of her past.

Following a personal attack at 14, Natalia was left feeling powerless, unable to control her life and what went on around her. The need for structure and something solid to hold on to became suffocating. Natalia began to restrict her food intake, driven by a need to take charge of the one thing she felt she could. 'The only control I had was over me, what I ate, and what I looked like.'

Having grown up around eating disorders and witnessed the devastating effects for myself, Natalia's story strikes a chord, which is painfully familiar. Yet, there's a part of me that can't help feeling like Natalia is holding back. I've read about the yearning for control countless times in reports, on websites and in forums. For me, it's the effect these rigid rules have that's harder to comprehend. Like poison, it seeps into every thread of thought, every sinew of self. As an outsider, you can only stand by and watch it happen.

To Natalia it became a familiar pattern. She didn't realise that these were the warning signs of something much sinister. 'I remember feeling very alone at first, that I was the only one in the world who felt this way.' But she wasn't alone. There are estimated to be 1.6 million people suffering from eating disorders in the UK, 10 – 19 year olds are believed to be the most susceptible, and the illness seems to be more prominent in young females. But these figures blur into insignificance when you are confronted with the reality of watching someone shrink before your eyes, both mentally and physically, to see them starve, day in, day out, governed by restriction.

By hiding her diminishing frame in baggy clothes and using inventive ways to skip meals, Natalia suffered in silence. By fifteen she was angry, confused and unsure of what was happening to her mind and body. The control she had felt in the beginning was starting to waver. There were limitations on how much she could physically achieve and it was stopping her from doing what she wanted. 'I felt very angry at the eating disorder itself as it was taking away my teenage years. While friends were out partying, I was too weak to get up or I was in hospital, so I missed out on a lot.'

Natalia's rules were supposed to construct a sense of calm and peace. To make her feel like she had stable foundations. A method of making sense of the chaos that engulfed her mind. But it didn't work. It never does.

Left untreated eating disorders can lead to severe health problems, such as heart conditions, liver damage and kidney failure. The body starts to shut down, turning off organs it doesn't consider vital. But medical definitions fail to describe the horror of the emaciated body. *A skeleton huddled in a corner, bony shoulders jutting out awkwardly shrouded in layers of clothing.*

After spending two years receiving inadequate medical attention through the NHS and with her weight reaching an alarmingly low level, Natalia's family took matters into their own hands. 'Because my weight was plummeting the only option we had was to privately pay for treatment.' Without this private care, Natalia was at risk of dying from her illness. Like so many other victims, she could have been robbed of her life; the one thing she was desperately clinging on to could have been stripped away. 'The private care did what the NHS didn't. It gave me treatment there and then and let me start to recover.'

Natalia's experience only tells one side of the story. With anorexia, pages of life are torn away. A chapter is never written and the blank sheets spill over into the narratives of those around you. As a bystander, the absence becomes imprinted. There is an empty space, a place that was supposed to be filled with memories, which has become nothing more than a white page.

The struggle is painful to witness and, overwhelmed by a natural urge, you want to help. But you're powerless. The lack of control is catching, the healing must begin with the sufferer and your hands are tied. Banished to the outskirts of their battle, all you can do is watch and wait. Hoping that the conflict will end and they'll come back to you in one piece.

One More Cube

Laura Blackhurst

———

Vodka

and orange with three cubes of ice.
Wait. There should be four. Bad things come
in threes.

Look to the left at the man's ice filled cup.

Shit. Caught me looking. Can't turn back
round. He'll think I'm a creep. Generous in
size. The man takes up two whole seats.

Do they weigh these people at the front of
the check-in queue while everyone else
shuffles awkwardly and talks about the
weather? Did he actually phone up and
admit in a nonchalant but humorous way that
he needed two seats all for his enormous bulk?

What balls if he did. I wouldn't fly at all if
those were the options. I don't even want to
fly. Even in my perfectly roomy, singular seat.
But I have to.

Must ask the air hostess for more ice. But
she will bring more than one piece of ice and
that will make five or six or even seven. It's
just too much ice.

Instead I blurt out while she hands out
peanuts five rows away,

'COULD I HAVE ONE PIECE OF ICE?!'

She carries on calmly, handing out snacks,
like this is as normal as the old dear in row
seven throwing up into the paper bag. She
disappears.

How. Fucking. Rude.

———

But she returns. Clasping a lone piece of ice between silver tongs, clonking it in the cup.

Four. Pieces.
Of. Ice.

Perfection.

Now, to drink. Touching the cup to my lips, I sip for one-and-a-half seconds. A fleeting gulp, just enough to quench my initial thirst, but not too long for the ice to pierce my forehead in a harsh ache. Lower the cup.

Fuck. It's happened again. Can't put it down.

Don't panic. Remember how to take those breaths. In for four. Hold. Out for four. Repeat. Try it again. Place the bottom of the cup on the tray and just... let go. It's easy, remember? Just like the doctor said. Lower the glass, tap the tray with it four times.

Can't let go. It doesn't feel right yet. Two-seater has started to stare.

Tap it five times on this go. Success. Placed it properly, I can let go. Yes! No one gets it though. It just has to... feel right. Y'know?

Must. Not. Panic.

An hour later I can't face taking another drink. My tongue battles against my clenched teeth in a bid for any drop of moisture. A result of nibbling fourteen nuts, each in two equal bites. Can't risk another cup related mini-drama.

Fourteen is my lucky number. It just has a nice, y'know, ring to it. Fourteen days in a fortnight, generic time period to go on holiday. Fourteen, number of my favourite dish from my local Chinese. Fourteen, the age of my first kiss. Fourteen, two times seven. Lucky seven twice must be double as lucky. A good number. A nice number. A safe number.

Is this plane safe? I sit in row thirteen. Unlucky thirteen. How did they know to sit

me here, close enough for fourteen to taunt me from behind?

———

I should have been quicker getting everything in order at home to get a better seat.

It was Missy's fault. If that bloody cat hadn't started molting all over the new carpet I wouldn't have had to get the vacuum out again.

But I do love that cat. It's nice to live with a cat. They never answer back.

Maybe someone deliberately got here early enough to steal my seat? My brain can't stop chanting
Unlucky thirteen
Unlucky thirteen
Unlucky thirteen.

My neighbour looks straight at me, eyes so fearful he very nearly gets out of his chair, but ultimately must decide it would be too much effort.

Oh for fuck sake. I've been saying it out loud.

'You don't believe in all that nonsense do you?' he eventually says in a rasping, smoker's type of voice. The I-am-definitely-sitting-beside-a nut-job look had disappeared from his mug, he must have dismissed me as a very, very bad flyer. 'Don't worry so much, planes are the safest mode of transport known to man.' He has one last chuckle and puts his headphones on and closes his eyes contentedly as if proving his point.

Whatever.

Don't trust him. Not when there is so damn much of him to trust in the first place.

What could be so unlucky about sitting in row thirteen? Mid-way through the flight is row thirteen going to singularly plummet to the earth while the rest of the plane stays intact and everyone cheers and hugs and exclaims: 'Thank God we weren't sitting in row thirteen! Everyone *knows* how unlucky number thirteen is!'

——

I make sure the level is at fourteen.

How many things exactly did I unplug
at home? The TV is *definitely* unplugged.
Amateur mistake not to start with the telly.
Everything is surely Unplugged, I checked and
double checked and triple checked. Everything
but the fridge. Who on earth turns their fridge
off? The television MUST be off. But...wait.
Have I switched every switch off? I had to
have taken every bloody plug out but how can
I be sure about the switches? Does it matter?
I'm not sure. Touch wood.

No. There is no wood. No one
makes an aircraft out of wood. Should
have brought a bit just in case. I think of the
little wooden leprechaun, Gary, that sits on
the mantlepiece at home. Sneaky little thing.
I don't care if I have to run up and down the
aisles screaming: 'PLEASE! Someone get me
some WOOD!'.

Spotted: an old man's walking stick on the
other side of the plane, he wouldn't mind,
I think he's asleep. But I can spy a child's
travel chess set through the gap in the seats
from the row in front.

Fuck it. I'm doing it.

I unbuckle my belt and ignore the little
seatbelt sign that is staring disapprovingly
at me from above. I slide my hand through
the gap in the seats of row twelve and reach
out to touch a wooden pawn, but instead
knock over the entire set in my eagerness.
Done.

I lean over to push the volume button up on
the miniature television screen in front of me.

Should have seen the steam seep out of the
mother's Medusa-like hair before
she leaned over her chair to glare at me. I

——

'What do you think you're doing?
Are you a maniac? Don't just stare at me.
My child has done NOTHING for this entire
journey! I can't believe this! Do you not have
a tongue? That's it, this is absolutely
ridiculous. I'm calling a stewardess. How dare
you! Excuse me, air hostess. EXCUSE ME!

Could I?

I only wash my hands fourteen times a day. I
would wash them more but then that
would total more than fourteen times.

God, I wish I could wash my hands. I could
almost feel them doused in the woman's
spit even though there couldn't possibly be
a drop on me. Could I reach for my hand
cleansing spray in my bag?

'Please can you wipe that little spot of spit
off your face madam?'

thought she would somersault right over and
join us. The row thirteen crew.

I know I should have been listening. I really,
really know that. But, I couldn't stop thinking
about the saliva. It was right there on the
corner of her lip, trembling every time she
screamed a couple of decibels louder. Slowly
sliding down her rouge face – a mixture of too
much blusher, too much anger and high blood
pressure. My hand clenched the miniscule
napkin they hand you with your equally tiny
drink. I couldn't possibly wipe it off her face
after what I'd just done.

But I couldn't just let it dribble down either.
It will drop over the seat onto our row.
People are crazy for not despising germs as
much as I do.

The air hostess's timely arrival meant I
couldn't enjoy her gaping, motionless face.
I thought someone had perhaps put her on
pause. The hostess only had to tighten her
drawn on, cartoon like eye-brows and purse
her lips like a disapproving teacher and I
knew I couldn't chat my way out of this one.

***

Well at least now I get extra leg room. It's bliss. Can't believe I managed to score this seat without paying extra. Some people try to avoid the exit seats. Row thirteen is now right over the other end of the plane. I'm all the way at the back. A curtain separates me from the rest of the germ-ridden inhabitants. I sneak a peek round and can still see the woman's crazy hair, be it very small. I think of waving to the large man to show him how good my new seat is. He has now moved to my old window seat. Bliss. I get extra room and get to be the first one out the door.

Hold the fucking phone. Did I *definitely* lock the door?

Vermouth
Katrina Patrick

They say that Churchill
Liked his martinis
With the bottle
Of Vermouth,
Waved
Over the glass.
He said it merely
Gave the idea
Of something
Else.

And I think that, maybe,
        That's how I love you.

Giants

Katrina Patrick

The tree
was a
tower.
Or sometimes,
A giant.
He could always climb -
Right
to
the
...top!
And survey
his whole
kingdom.
Or sometimes,
attack.
He spied on his grandfather –
arriving
with
a -
present!
A toy gun,
carved from
driftwood.
Or sometimes,
a snake.
Mam said his grandma,
who...
he
couldn't
...quite   remember,
Brought him
home-made
cookies.
Or sometimes,
a cake.

But they don't talk about her.
And he
didn't...
know
...why.

Hillsborough

Libby McInnes

———

Leppings Lane End was already an unmovable full before the boy and Da had arrived.

'Dez, where's Sweeney and Mike?' Da's pal with the moustache asked as the group snaked through the crowd.

'Workin', Dave. Miller asked me to stay late too but I told him it was my weekend with the lad,' Da said as he scruffed the boy's hair.

'Christ, they're gonna miss the first half coz the M62 is blocked.'

'Uh? Fuckin' road works on FA Cup semis day? Askin' for trouble, man. Askin' for it.'

Da kept his hand on the boy's head until they could move no further. Stopping, the boy arched upward from his tiny pocket of space taking in all the terraces of red and white. He wondered which team would be playing in away colours. He hoped it would be Forest. Red and white is best. And Liverpool is best. He craned his neck further and Da hoisted the boy onto his back.

'Better?' he asked smiling at the boy, a glint from his gold tooth.

The boy nodded. But it wasn't better. A vantage point he would never forget. He gripped his hands around Da's neck and watched the crowd stream in. Chanting became louder and faster. Crowd swaying. The announcer blaring.

'One. Bruce Grobbelaar… '

'Two. Gary Ablett… '

Cheering and clapping replaced singing.

A shift.

The teams rushed from the tunnel, but the boy was transfixed by something else. Confusion pumped his blood with a disturbing speed. A maelstrom formed at the front of the terrace. Over his shoulder the boy watched as more fans rushed to see the teams, smiling and swigging. Fans that rushed into spaces that didn't exist and couldn't be formed. With each new layer of people the crowd dominoed forward into the mesh fence. But no domino lay flat at the front of the pack for the rest to lean on. More fans. More pressure. Whistle blows. Game starts. Da already screaming at the ref. Only the boy could see.

'Da, Da… ' the boy tapped his father on the shoulder.

'What's up Johnny?'

The boy pointed down to the crammed crowd straining to pull back from the front. Father and son stared as carnage echoed toward them. They could both hear the screaming now.

'Christ on the cross, what the fuck's goin' on down there?' Da's tone scared the boy.

'Why the fuck they still lettin' them in?' Da pointed across to the opening at the centre of the terrace. Eyes lifted from the pitch to the angry mass of red pushing against itself. Whistling and screaming replaced singing. The flood of fans continued. Pushing and squeezing, no exhaling. Leppings Lane groaned under the red current of force. The boy gripped his father tighter.

'Fuck it, Johnny you're goin' up lad.' Da shouted at the boy, raw panic making it difficult for them to hear.

'What?'

'Up. I'm pushin' you up lad.'

'Na Da, I'm stayin' with you.'

'I'll be right up after lad, nowt to worry 'bout,' Da said pushing the boy toward a grabbing hand from the upper terrace.

The boy was pulled up with ease and stood with his tiny arms hanging over the barrier, reaching down with stretched fingers. A man with thick glasses pulled his shoulders back from the edge, his eyes darting to take in the trench below.

'No worries lad, we'll find ya Da' he said to the boy, who couldn't hear.

The boy peered below but couldn't see Da. No faces, but limbs, and red sucked inward. The mesh fence crumpled like a paper stitch and burst the pressure. Dominoes toppled flat. Screams rang in the boy's delicate ears. He inhaled and waited for Da to surface.

Golden Mushroom

Libby McInnes

Matthew stands at the window running his hands up and down the velvet curtain, chewing on his lip. One side of the curtain is rough and jagged under little fingernails, triggering a shiver down his spine. His eyes close. The other side is smooth, a soft release that allows him to escape for just a second. The light from outside streams in at a sharp angle as fibres from the curtain dance in a column of rainbow colours. Matthew blindly waves his arm through the light with fingers stretching wide to control the floating fibres. The threads explode with the invasion of a small hand but swiftly form again, destined to twirl in the single shaft of magnetic sunlight. Eyes open. Matthew stares at his brother. William is on the floor. Blackcurrant Ribena spilled, sticking and soaking into the rug, through the squeaky floorboards and down to where the mice live. Controller still in William's hand. Fingers twitching like he is ready to jump up and laugh and beat his younger brother. Maybe it's a new game Matthew hasn't heard of, the rules unexplained to him. But it's been a while now. Matthew chews on his lip again. Both karts have stopped on the screen as the seconds in the corner tick in frantic neon green. Yoshi and Mario are waiting to finish the race, looking over their shoulders to find a player in the room.

Matthew edges away from the window, a push from the windowsill lifting him onto tip-toes. The room is quiet, floorboards static. Spiderman and Batman watch from inside their posters. Matthew looks to them, imagines what they would do. They remain silent bursts of colour.

White cotton socks near the purple blemish, afraid of any red stains and what they may mean. His worried lip is now bleeding, oozing an unknown sweetness that Matthew doesn't like. He sits cross-legged infront of William, a hand on his shoulder pushing to and fro.

'Billlaay, I'm gonna beat ya, I just got a Golden Mushroom...'

Matthew whispers in his ear, hopeful. He picks up his controller and pretends to tap the buttons. His eyes remain on his brother. Yoshi stays frozen, like William. No flicker of a smile. Matthew holds his breath; the room completely paused for a moment. His cheeks are puffed, letting the air out slowly in a little 'o' shape to stall time. To stall understanding. Matthew kneels beside his brother now, urgent, and pushes his cheek in. A white fingerprint dissolves into William's pale face. Matthew moves closer, his ear on his brother's chest. He can hear it.

Du-dump, du-dump, du-dump.

It is slow. Matthew keeps his head there, hoping hard with clenched fists that William is still luring him in. If he scares him now he won't mind, he won't tell Mam, he'll let him win. He slaps William's cheek, softly at first and then harder. The hair on William's cheek is coarser and spiky under Matthew's palm. Uneasy like the curtain in the corner.

'Billlaay, you've got ten seconds to get up, I'm hawking up a real good one...'

Matthew collects all available phlegm from his mouth into one threatening mess on his tongue. He shuts his eyes tight, wishing to reset this game, scared nothing will change when he opens.

'Ten. Nine. Eight. Seven...'

Eyes unopened this time. He calls for Mam.

Clouds
Libby McInnes

———

The back of Jenna's legs stick to the leathery plastic of the chair, legs dangling and unable to touch the ground. Her pink jelly shoes are too bright for this place where colour is not allowed in because maybe it will make people happy. Jenna picks at the white stuffing which has burst from the corner of the leather chair she is sitting on. She joins so many anxious hands which have fumbled and rubbed and tugged and scratched this chair. She pulls at the stuffing, looking around to make sure no-one can see. She doesn't want to be a bad girl; Mama said she had to be good when she isn't watching. She burrows her hands deeper, pulling at the white fluff and balls it in her hands. It's like clouds, soft and springy. Like the big burst of whiteness she can remember from the blue sky this afternoon. She pulls the stuffing apart, spreading it into longer, more wispy clouds. It makes a lovely scarf for Floppity, her purple bunny who sits next to her on the chair. Jenna pulls back Floppity's head, arching his nose into the air. He can smell it too. Chicken soup. Not the nice kind that Mama makes, but an old kind that is not special and that everyone has. She thinks of it being mixed in a great big pot. One that would sit for a while and form a skin on the top. When people want to eat it, the skin would be mixed to the bottom and only the baddest people would get bits of this leather crust. Jenna giggles to herself as she imagines the bad people eating the bad soup. She swirls the stuffing back from around Floppity's neck, round and round between her palms as Daddy comes out of the door she is sitting next to.

'Jenna, you can go in and see Mama now. But just remember to be gentle, she's had a long day,' Daddy says.

Jenna holds Daddy's hand as her jellies squelch on the linoleum floor. She can hear the machine next to Mama's bed and watches the green line spiking up and down slowly. Jenna smiles as she skips toward the bed, Mama shifting her head across the pillow and down to her little girl and purple rabbit.

'Hi baby.' Mama says, her voice a soft croak.

Jenna hops onto the bed, her small hand gripping her mother's cheek as she kisses the other.

Mama looks whiter today, but it's okay because Daddy brought her make-up and she can put the nice red powder on her cheeks. Her eyes are heavy but it is dark outside so Jenna knows it is time for bed. Jenna squeezes the little ball of fluff in her hands and realises her Mama needs it more than the sticky chair outside.

'Mama, I know its bedtime, but I've got something really really really good for you,' Jenna says.

'Uh-huh, what's that?' Mama smiles quietly in Jenna's ear so that Daddy can't hear, pulling her daughter closer. A moment for the two of them. Mama inhaling the innocence of her daughter's blonde hair as Jenna twists the plastic bracelet, with words that she can't read, round Mama's wrist.

'Hair. I've got you some lovely fluffy white hair that's like clouds.'

Jenna produces the little white ball from her palm, smiling wider than her mother has ever seen.

Loyal
Stewart Brower

Two seconds oan the bus and there's awready a chant of 'Would ye like a chicken supper Boaby Sands?' I'm doon the front, squeezed in next tae The Kid. He's puffin oan a snout awready, chain smoker the cunt. Haunds me his boatle opener, I crack the lid and fuckin Miller comes shooting oot aw over ma new home tap. Magic.

I can see her blue eyes sparkling, even from behind her thick blonde fringe. She walks slowly towards me, managing to wring every tiny bit of sexuality out of her proportions. I know I'm smiling too widely, but how can I help myself? The smell of her perfume is strong but unobtrusive. It's just like her, feminine and classy. She sits close by and crosses her legs.

It's no long before the chico is gettin passed roond like naebody's business. Tenner goes right up ma hooter, and am tootin fur God and Ulster. Quality gear an' all, boy up the back a the bus always comes through wae the good shite. I pass the note onto big Daz. That cunt's eyes are rollin in the back a his heid n' no mistake. 'Hang Neil Lennon, hang him high,' comes the chant, and we're aw rattlin the windaes.

My arm goes around her shoulder and she likes it, burrowing deep into me. I look down as she looks up, our eyes meet and we both smile. I'm looking at the surface, admiring what I see, but she seems to be looking much further into me. I lean down and kiss her. She nibbles on my bottom lip, knowing I love that.

Stoatin up tae Ibrox, the sea a blue is fuckin majestic man. Makes ye so proud tae be a Teddy Bear. Wee Sproulie's goat a half boatle a tonic and he gies us a tan. Pure rank that stuff but gets ye steamin that's fur sure. Every cunt splits up ootside the ground, meet in the Glaswegian efter the game fur a proper Sash Bash. Me and Div head tae oor seats but no before that fat prick gets himself a pie.

I let myself slide down the couch onto my back, bringing her down on top of me. She throws her head up, bringing me eye level with her breasts. She knows all too well what she's doing to me. I roll my eyes up and she's got her serious face on, eyebrows raised. We've been here before. In our most practiced move I grab her waist and twist both of us round. Now I'm on top and she's smiling.

'Fur there's no a hair oan the Virgin Mary's fanny… ' Fuckin love that chant man, total hilarity. Oor bit's no bad, but atmosphere is pure pish in Ibrox these days. Nae cunt wants tae sing. Too many weans and auld coffin dodgers. Still drowning oot they Motherwell wanks but. Only about twenty a them and no a peep. Wee Naismith heids one in oan half-time but this game is shite and it's pissin it doon.

I softly kiss her cheek, before working down. She turns to the side as I reach her neck. For a moment I nuzzle her with my chin, and I hear her breathing grow louder. As I begin to kiss her roughly, I rub the small of her back with my forefinger and her leg twitches. She makes a small sighing noise and for a heartbeat our eyes meet, before she throws back her head.

Pure buzzin when we meet every cunt efter the game. 3-0 so we're aw in a good mood stoatin to the Glaswegian. Ma phone goes n' it's the missus textin us to see how we got oan. I dinnae bother textin back, cos Sproulie shoves mare Tonic into ma paw and I'm startin to feel proper fuckin swallied. I start a chant of 'We love the Rangers we do,' n' the whole fuckin street starts singing it. Love it.

She whispers in my ear, 'Bedroom?' and nothing else needs said. She grabs my hand and we're on top of her bed. I try to resist, try to be the gentleman, but my hand finds its way to her breast, and I'm pawing at her. My other hand runs along her curves, slowly down. I reach the fine material of her underwear, and greedily I pull it aside.

Glaswegian is packed, nae chance ae a seat. Aw ma boys are staundin at the bar and Div shouts me up a lager. Loyalist tunes are oan awready, King Billy oan the wa n' that and every cunt's up bouncin. Ma phone's goin aff in ma poaket and I know it's her but I cannae be arsed the noo. I get the round in and get maself a wee hauf to follow ma pint. It's time tae get smashed. 'Oh if ye cannae dae the bouncy you're a tim!'

As she glares up at me with want in her eyes I'm thinking about my sheer luck. As she grabs hold of my belt with both hands and hungrily pulls it off I'm thinking about how she's far too good for me. As she reaches into my boxers and caresses me I'm thinking about how this could end at any time. As she brings me into her I can think of nothing but loving her.

'You wantin fingered?' Smut shouts at the wee bird pickin up the glasses. Every cunt's laughin. Poor lassie isnae but. She's proper ragin, like she's ready to smash they glasses right into Smut's dish. Ye'd think she'd be used tae that shite. There's pished Bluenoses in here every fuckin week, and most of they bastards are well dodgier than we are, that's for fuckin sure. Kid chucks a snout ma way so I down ma pint in a wunner and follow him oot.

Sweat beads and rolls from our bodies. As I collapse onto the pillow I see it glistening on her breasts. With her, even the sweat seems oddly beautiful to me. She rests her head on my chest, and I stroke her long blonde hair, stuck to her head with perspiration. I move my thumb down to her mouth and gently stroke her lips. She runs her nails down my back.

Kid is giein me a load of shite in the ear aboot this bird he's seein but I cannae be fucked wae that shite the noo. This is meant tae be a lad's day oot. Fox is puttin oot big fat lines in the bogs and I dinnae mind if I dae. Am pure seein stars noo, bumpin intae every cunt as I try tae find ma seat. Pure growlers that's for sure, lucky I dinnae get ma cunt kicked in. Throw a pint doon ma gullet and Smut's sayin, 'that's mine ya dirty bastard.'

Before I've even had time to breathe in the new day I feel her rub my stomach. My mind floods with happiness, and I know in that moment that she is what I want. I want to have her, I want to know her, I want everything about her. But I say nothing. I just smile.

Ma heid is spinnin. Fox has fucked aff and took the gear wae him. The tunes are startin tae die noo, seems like nae cunt can be arsed singin. Fuckin matter wae them? It's only 12 o'clock the lightweight pricks. Now that fat boot behind the bar is shoutin last orders, 'mon tae fuck' I say. Phone's still goin aff in ma poaket. Where's ma jaiket?

She wraps my scarf around my neck then comes in close for a kiss. I want it to last forever, but it doesn't. She pulls away. I don't want to leave her for anything. She takes a tiny step back and smiles. 'You'll miss the bus,' she says and softly closes the door. She pauses for a second behind the frosted glass. I can still see the blue of her eyes.

Taxi draps me aff right ootside. I chuck the cunt a score n' tell him tae keep the change. Can barely staund as am walkin up the drive, pure dyin for a slash. Go to pull oot a snout but a've no got any left. Fuck it. I bang oan the door. Nae answer. This time I pound the fucker, hink the glass is just aboot tae break when the fuckin hing opens.

She's standing in front of me, and I love her so much.

Too Drunk to Fuck

Richard Hampton

———

'And the hills are alive with celibate cries,'
While I gaze and stroke your daunting thighs.
Washing machine livers,
Nervous quivers, withdrawal shivers and sickly slithers.
Aroused by nothing of beauty suggested
We hold our hearts and kidneys arrested
With gleaming palms and freezing water
We duck and dive and breech our endings.
You'll hold my hand and I'll hold my form
While dozing off unrested scorn.

You hop aboard and I'll say goodbye
To my softening and ill-quenching sigh
That begs for life and duty tomorrow
While guilt consumes myself – digested.

I'll reach for medicine and let it drown.
And you'll grudge off a hidden frown.
I'll drink and stink and let it ring –
Every copper in the bowl will join my sink.

Hands

Richard Hampton

There is black under their nails and there always is
But you don't know where it came from.
There are white dots on those nails
But you don't know how they stained.
They feel the chill of glass and raise it towards your lips,
They feel the warmth of flesh and draw it towards your hips.
You'll make a fist or one that's loose to satisfy all primal itch.
You'll make a welcome and meet your kind.
Rougher, smoother, cleaner.
Index and middle sharing love or unwittingly causing offence.

The love line, the wealth line, the life line, telling tales,
But all the tales unfolded now have black beneath their nails.

While it's Worth it

Richard Hampton

———

Hold her like a child
With undying affection.
Hold her – a sore pawed puppy
With genuine hurt.
Hold her like change of a twenty,

Hold her till it's out.
The clear air will cloud the meaning.
Hold her till you can hold on.
Hold her while it's worth it.

Standing in the Way of Control

Louise-Anne Geddes

———

"'You scurvy shyster bastard,' I said. "Watch your language! You're talking to a doctor of Journalism!'" If there was ever a line I wish I'd written, that would be the one. From *Fear and Loathing in Las Vegas*, one of the strangest books ever published, it is also one of the most extraordinary pieces of work to come out of America at that time. Not quite journalism and not quite fiction, the line between the two was obscured entirely by the emergence of the eccentric genius Hunter S Thompson. In spite of his reliance on drugs and alcohol, Thompson's gonzo journalism paved the way for a journalism far from the dry and purely fact driven content where the journalist had no role other than to facilitate. Thompson wasn't the first to disregard the boundaries between journalism and fiction, but his outrageous style and content helped to pioneer an innovative writing form which meant journalists were able to involve themselves, as opposed to observing like the proverbial third wheel. Gonzo was born, baby, and so was a whole different perception of journalism in the literary world.

Thompson's twisted report of the Mint 400 in Las Vegas is probably his best known work, although the word report is not appropriate. Mind-fuck is closer to the truth. He's pissed and stoned for the majority of the book, and on first reading it seems like this would be a beneficial state for all concerned. Thompson is the pivotal figure who broke down the strictly patrolled barrier between acceptable journalism and fiction, and who repeatedly returned to give it another good kicking until it was damaged beyond all repair. This was a necessary damage, like chips and gravy after a night on the piss, which allowed journalism to progress as a creative industry as opposed to yet another 500 words of yawn. Journalism has a responsibility to inform the ignorant masses, but who says that information has to be imparted without passion? Atmosphere gives life, and although elitists reject gonzo as not serious or worth respecting, it gave an industry struggling to engage with readers a much needed kick up the arse. *The Kentucky Derby is Decadent and Depraved* might not bear much journalistic weight as news, but you can be damn sure I would have been reading it to discover the source of the depravation. Thompson's provocative style deliberately obscures the lines between what is true and what is invention and if you can't handle it, he doesn't care. He's off somewhere getting high. So fuck you.

Journalism which has a self awareness makes us self aware as readers. How Thompson feels, what he sees, thinks and does affects us. I'm reading 'Hideous Music and the Sound of Many Shotguns... Rude Vibes on a Saturday Evening in Vegas', drinking a sizeable glass of rosé (method acting, you see, to understand the mindset of the work in front of me) with my feet on my desk. I can smell garlic from the kitchen, and the wee girl next door is chatting to herself in the back garden. I am aware. The stream of consciousness style of Thompson's work set a precedent, giving journalists more control than ever before by disgracefully enabling comment. The experimental nature of gonzo gives scope to move away from dry journalism, and to enjoy participation.

Is gonzo less trustworthy because of its participatory nature? In Thompson's case, participation isn't really the issue. His alcohol and drug misuse were well known, and he was particularly candid about this in his works. For this reason, it is doubtful that all the events he reports are true, particularly the pterodactyls flying around the corridors of the hotel at the Mint 400. But seeing the world through his somewhat clouded eyes brings a raw honesty to his work and the addition of these fucked up events adds to the value of what is entertaining reportage as opposed to straight journalism. Gonzo is driven by atmosphere and a playfulness which makes it compelling. Does this mean it can't be trusted? Possibly. Does this matter? Probably not. Thompson's importance as a journo is on a par with that of the subjects he covers, if not more so, and modern documentary makers like Louis Theroux and Nick Broomfield are directly influenced by his unorthodox participatory style. Theroux controversially participated in a documentary on pornography, which was ethically questionable and risky. In *Hell's Angels*, Thompson went on the road undercover with the Angels for a year, and the reportage which resulted was astonishing. He got under the skin of the organisation who were figures of terror and fear for Americans. Factual accounts can be frightening, especially when concerned with topics considered taboo and Thompson's style offered escapism, convincing people that they were just reading a novel. Irresponsible journalism? That's one for you to decide.

Thompson's works, twisted as they were, had a tenacity and bare-faced I don't give a fuck attitude. The impact of such an irreverent and experimental quasi-journalistic approach to writing was huge, and his influence is still felt today in the works of writers such as Nick McDonell, author of *Twelve*, whom Thompson feared would 'do for his generation what I did for mine'. He pioneered a freedom to write with no restraints, and he transcended the restrictive guidelines as to what was acceptable as journalism and as fiction. There are many who played a part in joining the two genres, but Hunter S Thompson did so in such a completely haphazard and unselfconscious way that what resulted could only be ground breaking. Many have been influenced by Thompson, but for me no-one compares to him today in terms of unabashed and completely unique gonzo writing. There is a Thompson sized space waiting for journalists to unshackle themselves from carefully controlled copy, and really let go. In a progressive and forward thinking society, we would expect to be able to use the word 'fuck' without causing mass apoplexy. I don't suggest that journalists smoke some crack before meeting deadlines, but letting go and participating in a writing form which is informative yet entertaining and brave would rejuvenate the literary hybrid Thompson helped to create.

'Do it now.'

A Nice Cup of Tea

Lynsey Cameron

———

There is nothing you can't solve with a nice cup of tea.

Boil the kettle. Pop the teabag in the cup. Grab a biscuit from the sideboard and pick a teaspoon up. Watch the water flow from clear to brown, jab the bag with spoon as it swims around, add sugar as necessary. One lump or two. Pour in the milk, just a splash will do.

Suffocate the bag on the inside of the cup. Watch its insides ooze out until it is golden enough. Then comes the obstacle course from the cup to the bin, the finger pinch, the spoon race or just a toss in the sink. The tea must not be too warm or you'll ruin the entire cup. A light burn on the roof of your mouth is the tea drinker's curse.

Now this is the important part of the tea's healing power, always sit down, chat with a friend, watch TV, watch the minute hand approach the hour. Both hands round the cup now, yes, smile and be happy.

Anarchy in the UK

Lynsey Cameron

———

Anarchy in the UK is saying no to a cup of tea. It is referring to a toilet as anything but a loo. It is a misplaced apostrophe. It is not having heard of Monty Python. It is talking in a library. It is smoking a cigarette inside.

It is dancing like no one is watching. It is dancing like everyone is watching and you don't give a fuck. It is telling her you love her and not caring who hears.

Anarchy in the UK is calling in sick. It is being late. It is disagreeing with Stephen Fry. It is refusing to talk about the weather. It is not knowing the words to Bohemian Rhapsody. It is having no change for the bus. It is not reading the Daily Mail.

Another grey Monday and the anarchists form an orderly queue outside the town hall. The anarchist meeting is about to begin. Right on time. The anarchists swing on their chairs and talk about how much they hate biscuits.

In the corner an anarchist sighs.

'Come on guys, I'm fed up of this. Why do I always have to take the minutes?'

The Cave

Martin Schauss

——

The entry to the cave was little bigger than a foxhole. Hidden deep in a desert, between rocks and stones, it almost seemed like the cave was consciously trying to evade its discovery. The two brothers had never seen nor heard of this cave, although they often crossed this desert. On the day this changed, the two brothers, who had rested on the nearest rock, left their horses to look at the hole in the earth they had stumbled upon. Although it wasn't wide, it appeared to the men that it was very deep and when they shouted swearwords down the hole, their voices echoed repeatedly within the vast void that they could see from the surface.

The younger one would fit more easily than his burly brother, so they decided he would go first. A sharp rock scratched his back and the blood stained his white shirt, but he didn't feel it in all his excitement. The older brother handed down two oil lamps. Slowly, he squeezed himself through the hole and soon stood next to his brother. The cave now glowed in a damp orange light as the brothers shone their lamps around in circles. On one side, the cave widened and descended into seemingly endless depths.

They decided to climb down the rocks leading into the darkness like granite stairs in the castle of a giant. The descent was strenuous and the men feared for their necks each time they had to drop down from larger rocks. They soon lost sense of time and, worn out, got rid of their backpacks, continuing with only one oil lamp between them. But never did they stop. Nor did they speak a single word. The lonely sound came from the tapping of their boots, but they soon didn't hear that anymore.

Sweat dripped down their noses but both men were shivering, as the cave grew colder the further they descended. They knew their oil lamp wouldn't last much longer. They would be left in the darkness. Neither man was hungry or thirsty after what seemed like days of descending. An outsider could have mistaken them for skeletons. Instinct drove them further and the silence hammered at their eardrums.

The brothers weren't sure whether their eyelids were open or closed after the light was gone. It didn't matter to them. The darkness was the same. And they knew the way. It went down.

The younger brother was the first to collapse. His ankles cracked against the hard rock and his skull broke open on impact.

The older continued. He didn't notice his brother's death, nor would he have recognised him.

His thoughts were empty when his legs gave way a few days later.

A moveable feast

Gabriella Bennett

A shark is half fish, half carefully constructed, highly intelligent being with a body evolved over millions of years to work as a fluid, membranous machine. The only creature in the world that truly understands the shark is the Pilot fish. This timid creature finds itself drawn towards the shark who dwarfs it in size and ferocity. Before meeting its shark, a Pilot fish may live a quiet sheltered life in the dark places of the ocean, hiding from predators among sea weed and cavernous coral reefs. However, a chance encounter can bring the pair together – then, the shadow of the shark's sinewy form casts a dark and temporary cloud along the sea bed over the Pilot fish, whose head is turned in one shivering movement. A magnetism between the pair is created, despite the obvious danger for the Pilot fish. Certain types of creatures are just meant to be together.

The Pilot fish floats up the current, mesmerised by the brooding charm of the shark and momentarily surprises it. The shark is unused to such a small flighty creature behaving in such a forward manner and decides to entertain it out of curiosity. Intuitively it knows that the Pilot fish is too special to be considered prey and too important to let dart away. As the Pilot fish reaches the shark's face, it accidentally coasts straight over the bridge of its nose, gently meeting the shark's coarse skin with the smooth underside of its body. This action causes the shark to enter a state of catatonic immobility, and after it regains consciousness its emotional defences are never the same again. Without quite knowing how it happened, the Pilot fish finds itself living alongside the shark as its constant companion, feeding off the ectoparasites from leftover morsels of food at its mouth and alleviating it of its chronic toothache. Swimming together, the shark's large grey bulk only highlights further the Pilot fish's beauty. Like a flexing, gelatinous halo around the shark's head, its silvery stomach glints in the underwater haze and sometimes throws the kind of prism of light over the shark that only these two creatures can see. The Pilot fish has unmistakable colouring – its ostentatious stripes catch the eye of other sea dwellers and provoke envy in other small fishes. It flits around the shark at every opportunity in order to remain constantly on guard for other fish who might try their luck, unaware that none would dare.

The Pilot fish swims like an adoring gangster's moll alongside its shark and enjoys the protection that the king of the sea allows. In return, the shark is well looked after. The shark remembers the days before the Pilot fish and they were not as good as these. Since meeting the Pilot fish, the shark remains free from illnesses caused by its previously unscrupulous hygiene standards. Throughout the course of their time together, a Pilot fish elicits fragile and intrinsic details about a shark. What surprised the Pilot fish the most when it first found out is that when a shark attacks, it feels so disgusted and afraid at the violent act it is carrying out that it avoids looking at its subject at all costs. This self-revulsion causes its eyes to roll back in its head. In films, a shark thrashes wildly while attached to a bleeding creature in rose tinted water and its eyes are fixed firmly away from what it is doing. While it clamps a contorting seal in its two monstrous jaws, the shark slips away to daydream about how its Pilot fish looks when sleeping, or the way that stalagmites of seaweed feel against the body when swum through. The pitch black iris slides sideways to reveal a pale crescent shaped slit of eyeball as secret and unexpected as the shark's inner humility.

When excited by the thrill of a chase, a Pilot fish's belly pales from black to silver like a backwards blush. It enjoys attacks far more than the shark and vicariously lives out the pleasure of being born with razor-edged teeth. It busies itself afterwards with cleaning the blood and fibrous fragments from between the shark's rows of teeth as swiftly as possible so that the shark will not have to suffer the anguish of what it has just done for any longer than is absolutely necessary. The Pilot fish works methodically on each jaw and, over time, develops a taste for flesh. It has been known to persuade its shark to perform frenzied and pointless killings just for the hysteria. After attacks, the shark grows weary and emotional and must doze again to forget. The pair cruise together in the depths of the ocean, slowed in body and mind by the gentle heaviness of shared sleep.

It is a little known fact that when a shark is caught, the Pilot fish mourns for it by following the ship that has captured it. While the shark lies blank eyed and bloody on a glass bottomed boat, the Pilot fish attaches itself to the underside and desperately continues to try to clean its teeth. For up to six weeks it remains stuck to the ship, its mouth forming a suckered 'o' of shock, unable to prise itself away to eat. It is not uncommon to see a coasting shark and a Pilot fish swerve suddenly to avoid the emaciated and solitary corpse of another Pilot fish falling through the water from a boat on its final journey to the sea bed, in case it spoils the life they have created together.

Kelvinbridge

Lesley McKeran

———

The wee old man sitting next to me
has started his day with a whisky
Or two... or three.

He uses his stick to push himself up
knees bent, legs spread;
his great balancing act.

He offers his seat
to a woman half his age.
Chivalry exists.

Then the tube stops
and Chivalry gets off
at Kelvinbridge.

St George's Cross

Lesley McKeran

———

The **advert**
            I'm reading **at** St George's Cross
Is weirdly written.
                    Some words are bigger and **bolder** than others
                            And there are awkward **indents**
So the sentences sound funny
When I read them in my **head**.
                    So I read them again.
And again.
                            until it sounds right.

Buchanan Street

Lesley McKeran

——

A man stole a chainsaw.
Hid it down his shorts.
So the Metro says.
A chainsaw.
Down his shorts.

In Glasgow,
You see a guy
with a chainsaw down his shorts,
you notice it
and you ignore it.

He carries on walking down Buchanan Street
with a chainsaw down his shorts,
until some kid points and says
 'Hey mummy, why's that man got a chainsaw down his shorts?'
And mum tugs the child's arm
 and shushes him and looks the other way
And the kid says
'Hey mister, why've you got a chainsaw down your shorts?'
And the man gives a shifty look,
put his hands in his pockets and blushes a little
And mum blushes back,
shrugs her shoulders with an embarrassed wee laugh:
'Kids, eh?'
And the man shrugs back
with an embarrassed wee laugh:
'Kids!'

Backwards From Ten

Lynsey Cameron

'We'll count you down okay?'
My hand is enveloped by Mum's. Twice the size
of mine. Soft.
'Mum? Will you stay?'
My face is squinting now. Scared.
'Of course, baba.'
'The whole time?'
'Yep.'
He is talking now, the big man with the mask
and the coat. He doesn't seem very nice.
'You gonna count with us wee yin?'
I look to mum, she nods.
I push my fingers into the creases of her palm.
We count backwards from ten.
Ten
Nine
Eight
Seven
Si-
No one ever gets past six. I know that now.

There are books in the waiting room and a fire engine. I like looking out
of the window there. The stairs to the dentist are pink. It smells like
toothpaste. Mr Lamont gives me stickers. The lady at the desk always
smiles at me. She even knows my name.
'Hi Lynsey.'
I smile. I've just brushed my teeth with Mum so I know they look clean.
'Hi.'
I lean back on the magic chair. I say AAAAAAH. Mr Lamont says numbers
and letters. He asks how I'm doing at school but I can't talk because his
hand is in my mouth, poking at my teeth. Why does he do that? I'll ask
Mum later.
He is saying things to Mum that I'm not supposed to hear. He is calling
her Kath. I hope I get a sticker.
They have stopped talking now. The seat is bzzzzing back up.
'Mr Lamont says you have to go Glasgow to get some teeth out. Okay?'
I don't know what I'm supposed to say, I just want a sticker.
'Do I get a sticker?'
They laugh and I don't know why. They say I'll get a sticker. They say
something about weak teeth, namel and ribena.

Mum talks to the lady at the desk.
The lady asks if I'm going to be brave. I shrug. My sticker has a dog on it.

My mouth tastes funny. Sweet but not like sweeties.
Mum is still holding my hand.
'Were you here the whole time?'
Mum and Dad look at each other and smile. I'm sleepy.
'Do I get to go home now?'
Mum and Dad say I get to go home now. The man with the mask is putting his gloves in the bin. We say bye to the man.
Dad says he'll carry me to the car. I like that.
I normally manage to fall asleep before we get to the car, but not today. My mouth feels funny. Kind of empty. Still got my front teeth though. I checked.

It hurts now. It hurts where my teeth used to be. My eyes hurt from crying. Mum looks sad. Dad says he's got a present for me though. I like presents.
My eyes still hurt.
Dad has a bag from the Early Learning Centre. I like the Early Learning Centre. Me and Mum always go when we are in Glasgow.
I put my hand in the bag. I'm trying not to think about my teeth, that's what Mum said to do.
The toy is plastic but quite soft. I can feel its tiny hands. It looks furry but it feels hard. It's a gorilla but it has a little gorilla on its back. Dad says it's like when he carried me to the car. I tell Dad that is silly, Dad isn't a gorilla and I'm not a gorilla. He tells me the big gorilla is the Daddy gorilla and the little one is like me. I'm sleepy again.

There is red stuff on my pillow when I wake up. Sweet but not like sweeties again. Doesn't hurt anymore though. I'm wearing my favourite jammies. They have a clown on them. I don't have to go to school today. I kick at the top bunk. I tell Rainy about the red stuff. She gets the top bunk cos she's older than me.
'Muuuuuuuum. Lynsey's got blood on her pillow. It's gross.'
I make sure Rainy tells her it's red.
Mum tells Rainy it's not gross and that I've been very brave. Then Mum gives me a hug.
'What did they do with my teeth Mum?'
'Why don't you look under your pillow and see.'
'Cos there's red stuff on it Mum.'
'Maybe there's a surprise under it too... from the tooth fairy. We put your teeth under there before you went to sleep remember?'

I don't remember.

Mum is weird sometimes but I look anyway. A fifty pence. And another one!

'MUM THERE'S PENNIES UNDER HERE'

'They're from the tooth fairy.'

 I show Calum at school my gums. I go AAAAAAH. I tell him about my big teeth and the tooth fairy. He says the bin fell over yesterday and Katie got stung by a bee. I'm sad I missed that. I'll tell Katie about the tooth fairy, that'll cheer her up. The bee stung Katie's arm. It has a big red lump on it. Katie seems to know a lot about bees.

'Bees die when they sting people. Did you know that?'

I didn't know that. I'm going to tell her about the tooth fairy again.

'My Mum says some people are so allergic to bee stings that they die. Did you know that Lynsey?'

I didn't know that either. I don't think I like Katie very much. I show her the gorilla Dad got me. She says it's cool. Now she's talking about bees some more. I hope my big teeth grow in soon.

 'You don't have any teeth to grow into the space you see.'

He is showing me an x-ray. I'm missing a double period of maths for this. X-rays and a day off school. This is awesome.

'So you'll have to get the front two out to allow the new teeth to grow into the space.'

'So I'll have no front teeth?'

'It'll take around a month for your incisors to fill the space.'

I'm not sure I believe him.

He shows me the x-ray again and Mum tells me it's genetic. I'm not impressed. No amount of gorillas will make this okay. Mum takes my hand. My fingers are longer than hers now. My palm smothers hers.

'It's only teeth, I guess they'll grow back.'

'Braces? That'll be right. I had no front tooth for three years Mum. He told me one month, on that timescale I'd be in braces for...'

I have to pause to do the maths.

'36 years Mum. Thirty six bloody years. I could die wearing braces. I would graduate with braces. On the plus side, no worries about braces in the wedding photo, because no one would marry me if I had braces. Mum, he is mental.'

'I think you're overreacting. If he says it's the best thing, you might regret saying no.'
'I think I'd regret having braces at 21.'
'Well he's the orthodontist; he's only trying to tell you what's best. You only get one set. Wish I'd looked after mine.'
Braces at 21. Bloody mental.

 I can't sleep. The pain is marching from my lower jaw up and up to the cartilage of my ear. It teases round the curve of my temple and forces my eyes open.
4:59.
Too early to get up, too late to go out.
Fuck it.
Count backwards wee yin.
Ten
Nine
Eight
Seven
Six
Five
Four
Three
Two
Fuck

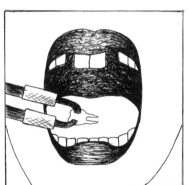

I guess it's easier to get past six without the gas.
A little more painful too.
No gorillas.
No blood on the pillow.
No tooth fairies.
No hand to hold.
You only get one set.

Reign Rose

Julie Shennan

———

Rain pelts down on the way to the Ramshorn Theatre, my mascara and I begin to run. This is not everyday rain, more like the kind Noah faced before he got his arse on that ark. Rain soaks through my jacket, behind my glasses, and by the time I reach the front door I'm an Alice Cooper lookalike.

Momentary relief hits as I step inside. But it doesn't last long. There is a palpable tension in the air, like the first hour of a birthday party. Will anyone come? In this rain? The MC voices my silent doubt, 'We were worried no one would make it,' he jokes, but not really. Gratefully, I receive a plastic cup of wine, and glance around. We are waiting for more to arrive before starting the reading. The tension comes, not from the small crowd, but from its obligation to socialise. God, I hate mingling. I face the familiar decision: attempt integration and risk rejection, or take an antisocial seat? I take a seat. I see Dilys Rose, also sitting, and relax: if the guest author's doing it, it must be okay. She and two girls crowd round the candy coloured table; daughters maybe. I meet her eye, smile slightly. I interviewed her earlier today, so we kind of know each other, but don't. Like a one night stand.

I look away at the decor, plain paint walls, dolled up with mood lighting. It's a Glasgow skyline trick; purple and turquoise beams to make the ugly attractive. A 'drip, drip' echoes from the false ceiling. The drip persists like a clock, hurrying us up. Sympathy nerves start. I only met Rose today, but I'm worried for her. She strikes me as insecure; like the ceiling. Drip, drip. There are people, hustling noises, and the MC declares the night a go. Rose takes the floor. I hold my breath. She dons a prop hat and starts, and that's it. She's a different person, confident, not the woman I interviewed.

'The weather was permissive... ' Rose drawls, reading her poem, not reality. She attributes the phrase to a Slovakian tour guide's broken English. Bad translation creating good poetry... now there's a use for Google Language Tools. Rose explains her writing as part recollection, part invention: 'Writing is about what you observe around you... you always have to take what you know of the world and then do something with it.' In this case 'something' is adding a camp voice which exclaims, 'It was a day for gluttony, sloth and perhaps pride.' Dorian Gray would approve. Like the fabled aesthete, Rose tells how her life was changed by art:

'Before I started writing I did a lot of drawing and painting; I probably wasn't very good at it. Then when I had been travelling for a while, in my mid twenties, I lost a whole series of drawings on a bus. I realised that if I was going to be so unsettled it might be better to work in a form easier to reproduce. That's when I started writing.'

And write she did. In 1989, Rose broke into the literary scene with *Our Lady of*

Pickpockets, a collection of short stories, and *Madam Doubtfire's Dilemma,* a collection of poetry. She shrugs off my dramatic metaphor, saying 'It looked like I had been really prolific, but they had been worked at over quite some time.' Rose rejects the anecdote of overnight success, 'It didn't really happen like that, the process for me was very slow. I was writing poetry and short fiction and gradually things were getting published in magazines, and broadcast on radio. Then, at the end of the eighties, my book of stories and book of poems came out at the same time.'

Since then she has written a novel, three collections of short stories, and four of poetry. But her heart belongs to poetry, she explains, 'For me it is about sound and music, I deal with poetry in prose as much as in verse.' Highlighting the tragedy of such love, she says, 'There has never been a lot of money in poetry and some people say there is not a lot of poetry in money.' With a one liner like that, she owns the stage.

Watching her poise and tone shift with her words, I note that they seem well suited to the stage. It is no surprise then, that Rose was librettist in Rory Boyle's Opera, *Kaspar Hauser.*

'That was a great collaboration, really enjoyable in all respects. The composer and I had worked on a piece together before, and had been talking about doing something again. He mentioned he had been reading a book about feral children, and Kaspar Hauser's story stood out, which was one that had always interested me. We were fortunate enough to be given the *Creative Scotland Award,* and to have a director who was very accepting of what we wanted to do, which was to keep it understated.'

The same cannot be said for Rose's previous musical production, *Helter Skelter.* Staged in the Tramway Gardens, with contortionists and cabaret dancers, it was described as a 'dark fairytale for adults'. Rose sighs recalling; 'It was one of the most stressful things I have ever been involved in. When it came to staging there were terrible problems with the venue, it rained that whole summer, and it was an outdoor production. There were some great ideas, but it was not ready when it was first put on and people kept trying to squeeze it into a narrative. It was conceived as a sort of round idea of fairgrounds and other things to do with childhood. Each individual piece of work was supposed to be considered on its own, and what then happened was the director wanted to make a full narrative out of it... ' she trails off, lost in memory.

Experience has shaped her writing through the years. She notes her style has mellowed from its feminist roots, adding dryly, 'I'm not a man hater, I like the man... that's not to say he always likes me.' Despite this disclaimer, feminist humour still shines through Rose's poems. At no point is this more apparent, than when she reads *Surrealist Shopping List,* waxing, 'Woman with her breasts out, woman with her throat out... severed limbs, floating limbs, ugly erotica, inside jokes.' In case we didn't get the message, she clarifies, 'It was a very interesting Era, the Surrealist, but very sexist.'

With no romantic allusions about the past, Rose admits she hasn't done much writing on period fiction, a habit which she is breaking with her latest novel. She explains, 'It's about the last person to be hanged for blasphemy in Scotland. His name was Thomas Aikenhead and he was a student in Edinburgh at the time... I have enjoyed the research, but I am writing this, not so much because I want to escape into the past, but because the story of a man betrayed by his friends and sent to the gallows is worthy.'

Equally worthy, is Rose's pending project, an autobiographic account of a father/daughter relationship, and its maturation through time. She explains the motive for writing such a personal piece now, saying, 'The way you see life changes as you get older, especially when you have children.' Rose admits these days, she is happiest when enjoying a good meal with family.

Tame as this family life may seem, I have to admire her as she soberly recites, 'Her vagina was pay as you go,' inches away from her maybe daughters. Doesn't even blush. The woman has more balls than I thought. I smile, envious of her maturity. I'd die if my mum said that.

As the night ends, we clap, breathe a sigh of relief. The ceiling is still standing, albeit with buckets underneath. Rose stops by on her way out of the door. 'Thanks for coming,' she says.

'No bother, you were really good,' I smile, and hope I don't sound surprised.

Golden delicious woman
Gabriella Bennett

———

I
am
now
dead
flesh.
Inside
bruises
occurred
following
redefining
exceptional
circumstance.

Little parts
Gabriella Bennett

———

We were waiting for the tube at Ibrox after being out the night before (six pints of Deuchars each, Cher karaoke at the Kenny) and getting impatient at the eleven minute wait (outer circle suspended again, second time this week) when you put your mouth against my head and blew hot air against my shaved hair (calling on the backs of my knees to tingle and pay attention like last night) while I closed my eyes and pretended that a small spot of sun had found me underground. And I was thinking about the first time we met and how in the morning I'd tried to remember your face but it kept slipping in my mind all the time as if I could only hold each of your features in my mind one at a time. I could picture your nose (slightly snubbed like your Swedish father living in hospital) and the small of your back (where fourteen other women's nails had dug in before mine) and the scar on your cheek (from teenage acne, matching the one on your thigh) but all separately. I was thinking about that morning and how I didn't know any of the stories behind each part which made it impossible to link them all up and make one solid image that meant anything to me. As the train pulled in and paled the tunnel, you held my hand and we got on, packed in between dozens of other people we didn't know.

Ready

Richard Hampton

———

They walked arm in arm with his hand under her coat and around her waist. Smiling and laughing, joking and kissing. They talked of their futures and the next time they'd meet up. They walked like all the couples along Sauchiehall Street.

'We shud go in thair some time, ma flat mate raves aboot the place,' said Michael as they walked on to George Square.

'Yeah we shud!'

'Aye, we shud,' he said as they stopped for a long kiss outside his flat.

They made it back to his room and began kissing; stripping each other with lips barely untangling, she pulled off his t-shirt and he pulled down her dress. He threw her to his bed, pulled down her pants. He touched her, testing the water. It was just right. He pulled back slowly, ready.

'Michael? Michael?'

'Whit!?'

'Put oan a joanny.'

'Eh... ah.' Looking at his dresser, 'I dinnae huv any, I'll jus pull oot win Ah'm aboot te, Ah promise.'

'Okay Michael, make sure ye dae bit.'

'Course ah wull,' he said with a smile, and with care pushed into her. Wendy felt the break, winced and hoped no blood would come. Michael pushed harder till there was no place left to push and began the rhythm. They kept eye contact, but with concentration rather than intimacy. He grabbed one breast and pushed it to her neck as if he was seeking a firmer foot-hold. Wendy tried hard not to look uncomfortable and simply repeated a half satisfied, 'ugh'. Michael grabbed her pony tail and pulled hard until she was facing the headboard, he sucked her exposed neck. He let go and buried his head in the pillow allowing Wendy the relief of a facial contort. He began to drive furiously building up higher and higher moans until he halted.

'Ah'm soarry.'

'Why Michael?'

'I couldnae help it, it was too much.'

Wendy rushed to the bathroom and taps could be heard roaring. Michael rolled on to his back and smiled.

'Wit te fuck! Why the fuck dindya ye tell me you were oan the fuckin' rag!?'

'Oh... eh... soarry, Ah thought Ah'd a few mair days.'

'Well ye coulda fuckin' well hud a wee wash before like.'

'Ah'm soarry Michael.'

'Mon tae bed Wendy.' She walked in quickly with an arm across her breasts and jumped in, pulling the duvet to her neck.

'Ah'm no sleepin' on that side Wendy, it's all blud' said Michael as he rolled to the clean side of the sheet.

'Blud and wank Michael, can we no spoon?'

'Ah get too warm, away te sleep.'

Wendy set an alarm for 8am, she had class in the morning. She arched herself around the pink puddle as best she could.

* * *

'Wit the fuck's tha?' groaned Michael.

'It's jus' mah alarm, Ah've class te go te, do you no?'

'Off Mondays,' he said as he rolled over.

'What's yer number Michael?'

'Dunno, jus' goughtta new Sim.'

'Well why dinnae you ring ma number and I kin get yours, it's oh siven eight, two siven...'

'Fuck up will ye, Ah'm trying te sleep, there's a pen there oan the desk, write it somewhair.'

'Okay Michael,' said Wendy as she pulled up her dress and looked for her tights. She found a pen and scribbled down her number on the front of his Sport Science file. She went over and kissed Michael on the cheek expecting one further on the lips.

'Ah thought you said you didnae huv any joannies?' she said looking at the dresser.

'Oh... shit, soarry there. Ah forgot about thum.'

'But you looked at your dresser last night. Lookin for them.'

'Ah forgot.'

'But they're right there,'

'Ah fuckin' forgot alright.'

'Okay Michael.'

'Cheerio then.'

'Talk soon eh? Text me later? You can ring us if you like, I'll be out from three.'

'Aye. Bye now.'

Wendy walked to the front of his flat, took a pair of flat shoes from her bag and put on her coat. She flagged a taxi.

'Gud night then hen?' said the taxi driver.

'14 Emma Street.'

'Alright luv.'

Wendy took out her mobile phone. She held the number four until it began ringing.

'Hiya Rachie, did muh Ma ring las' night?'

...

'Thank fuck, got away wih it then.'

...

'I'll fill you in later. Have you dun yer work fer Andrews?'

...

'Nah me neither, right I'll talk to you when I get in, just comin' up the hoose the noo.'

...

'See ye soon,' said Wendy as she came up to her house.

'That's six fifty darlin.'

'There's siven.'

'Cheerio love.'

14 Emma Street, when she was younger she looked forward to the day her house number would match her age. One of those childhood nuances that never seems to escape memory.

Wendy crept up to her house with her coat buttoned to her knees. She checked her phone, unlocked the door and went up the stairs.

'How wis Rachael's then Wendy?' She heard her mother shout from the kitchen.

'Fine Ma, Ah'm just gonnae jump in the shower.' Wendy walked into the bathroom and reached for her toothbrush and squeezed a sweep of toothpaste on the brush. She stared at the red and white stripes. She brushed and spat without looking. She stepped into the shower; washed her hair and washed herself, making sure all was clean after last night. She sat on the toilet seat and looked down. It was still sore but she knew it would be, everyone said it would, but it was good after you got it out of the way. She'd gotten it out of the way but that was all. No gentle carresses, whispered loves, slow, long, nibbled necks or concerned eyes. No heads on chests and fiddling hair.

'You're gonnae be late Wendy.'

'Ah'm just getting out now mum.'

'Are you alright?'

'Aye, I just fancied a long one.'

'Right oh, there's tea and toast waitin for ye.'

'Thanks mum.'

She stood up and washed again and when she felt clean enough, she tucked a towel across her chest.

She dried herself in her bedroom, pulling out her hairdryer and sweeping its warm winds across her closed eyes. Her phone buzzed; she dropped her hairdryer and ran to her dresser. Gary. Year above. She pulled on a clean white pair of pants. She pulled up her knee-length black socks. She glanced in the mirror and looked at her phone, blank from inactivity. She squeezed into her short black skirt, buttoned her shirt and knotted her red and black tie while reaching for her phone again.

'He's probably still in bed.'

Dog
Catherine Baird

behavioural problem one
sits in his doggie basket
purple plastic
chewed rim
scratches at his side with his back paw,
pops his lipstick out
pants
wanks himself off
into his doggie blanket
brown fleece with images of bones.

Deterioration of the Fight or Flight Response
Louise-Anne Geddes

He hears what he thinks is a car backfiring. There is a moment of absolute stillness. Nothing happens. A woman begins to scream, and a person pushes her to the ground before running away. He goes to her and offers his hand, but she is unaware of him. All she is focused on is the person lying on the ground, unconscious and bleeding. The contents of her handbag lie scattered across the ground. Sirens begin to scream in the distance, and the woman struggles to her feet. He looks at the face of the man on the ground. The face is his own. His body, his hands, his feet, his bleeding chest. He shouts. No one hears him. An ambulance screeches into the street, followed by a police car. The ambulance crew rush past him, making him stumble. He swears and leans against a sycamore tree, watching. Waiting. He digs a hole in the ground with his toe as the paramedics assess the two bleeding wounds on his chest. He feels no pain.

'Pain is irrelevant to survival.'

A small crowd has gathered. 'Cool! He has a hole in him!' A little boy is shushed by his father, who stands with his mouth hanging open. The woman is no longer screaming, but sobbing uncontrollably. A female police officer puts an arm around her trembling shoulders. He cannot hear her words, but they don't appear to be having any effect on his wife. The paramedics lift his stretcher into the ambulance. The crowd disperses. His wife climbs into the back of the ambulance, and just as the doors are closing he climbs aboard as well. He waves into his wife's face, but she cannot see him. She stares at a space on the wall. He looks at his body on the stretcher. The paramedics speak in low hushed voices. His shirt is ruined, blood stained tatters lying forgotten on the ambulance floor. He prods his damaged chest. He feels no pain.

The ambulance wails into Accident and Emergency. The paramedics open the doors. He jumps out quickly and steps aside. He watches. They rush into the building, his wife running desperately behind them. Sighing, he sees a tired young nurse leaning against the hospital door, smoking:

'Any chance I could pinch one, hen? God knows I could use it!'

He chuckles to himself, and holds out his hand. She ignores him, and throws away her cigarette, rushes back inside the building. He follows her. He finds his wife standing outside the Resuscitation Room, her face pressed against the glass. He peers over her shoulder, and watches as doctors, nurses, surgeons and people, lots of people try to save him. He winces at the mass of blood and meat that was his chest. He feels no pain.

'Fragmentation of the bullet may produce secondary missiles, one or more of which may have exit wounds.'

He passes two police officers in the corridors. They approach his wife. He steps aside and listens. They look distinctly uncomfortable. The policeman clears his throat: 'We've recovered the weapon. It was discarded in some bushes around a mile away from where your husband was attacked,' he fiddles with his notebook, his tie, his ear. 'But we've nothing to go on for the attacker.'

He watches his wife. She looks older, like her own mother. He decides that he can't put her through any more of this. He will just die, and it will all be over. He will feel no pain. She will feel no pain and it will be easier for her. He takes one last look at Mary, kisses her cheek and walks away. She puts a hand to her cheek.

'The body engages survival patterns: the well known fight or flight syndrome.'

There is an outburst of bleeping noises from the room. Doctors are shouting 'we're losing him,' and 'his BP is dropping'. He pauses, but keeps walking away. He likes it where he is. He feels no pain.

The policewoman once more puts her arm around Mary's sagging shoulders. Mary lifts her head, and with a fierceness which catches the policewoman off guard, she shouts: 'He'll pull through this! I know he will, he'll do it for me!'

He turns round and realises he has no choice. He must go back. He must live. He can't expect Mary to do this on her own. She needs justice to be done and he is pretty pissed off himself! His new shirt is ruined. He has made up his mind. He smiles at himself, and walks back towards the room where he lies opened out like a gutted pig. He is back. He is back. He has to live! But how can he fight when he is out here?

The sounds of emergency coming from the room begin to subside. For almost fifteen minutes, doctors have been trying frantically to save him, bring him back. There is no hope. It is too late. He is too late.

Mary stands outside the room, broken. He takes a deep breath and throws open the door. He goes to the side of his body. He closes his eyes and lies down. The monitors pick up a faint heartbeat. He can vaguely hear the staff gasping and bustling to treat him. He smiles. The pain is beautiful.

Pigeons/Columba Livia

Lynsey Cameron

———

Hard time living on the streets little fella?
You and this city grew tired together.

They hate you,

You know it,

It's their waste that feeds you,
Their children that chase you,

They're the ones calling you names.
RATS WITH WINGS
THOSE HORRID THINGS
THE WORST KIND OF BIRD
bet they can't even sing.
Little do they know,
Fella.
Cos they never see you at night.

Up,
High,
On your rooftop terrace,
The humans become scavengers,

The city and them tired together,
Getting revved up

Getting high

together.

They can get high one drink at a time,
One pill at a time
From one puff
or from
one
line.

But you,
Little fella,
You'll always have the wings.

———

'In Glasgow,
You see a guy
with a chainsaw down his shorts,
you notice it
and you ignore it.'

Lesley McKeran

The Toothbrushes in My Bathroom

Cameron Steel

The toothbrushes in my bathroom
are up to something – I'm sure of it.
Every time I open
the door.

There they are.
Leaning back, reclining,
relaxing
stood, still, smiling.
Frozen.

They were all chatting before I opened
that door – I'm sure of it.
Pointing their heads, craning their necks, this
way and that way – those minty giraffes!

Having a laugh. At my
expense.
I'm sick to the

back teeth of it.

Kiss Collision Lovers

Lauren Deegan

——

We live in a castle in a quiet wooded area on the coast of England. It has lush gardens decorated with romantic statues and topiary animals, and seven bedrooms, all with beautiful en-suite bathrooms and knives lining the ceilings. Tall fir trees shroud it in a haven of security. The glass walls are coated with blood and rose petals litter the floor. This is a Valentine's paradise, where the Kiss Collision lovers come to die.

Population growth is out of control. If the human race continues to multiply, we will all be extinct within the next twenty or thirty years. Food supplies are already showing signs of diminishment and people are murdering each other to get their foot on the property ladder. Put in this context, our project can be regarded as a romantic means of scraping away the limescale of society – a type of Euthanasia for love. Kiss Collision services are well known throughout certain circles of the nearby territory. Those who trawl underground clubs, or see those bands no one else has even heard of, they all know us.

The government are well aware of our project: they even give us financial support and advice for discreet advertising. They view the whole underground scene as a threat, and would much rather support a mass culling than risk political anarchy. We are not the only community of our kind in the UK, but we are different, because we offer death for two.

We mainly cater for couples to whom hostility and malevolence is an external by-product of their relationship – those lovers who are torn apart from each other as a result of jealousy, religion, family, friends or enemies. When no one wants you to be together in this life there is always room in the next.

Sometimes we are visited by individuals who have lost their love through accident or illness and cannot face living anymore: a brigade of broken hearts who need them finally shattered. This is okay, but there are certain boundaries to what we will accept. Firstly, both parties must be above the legal age of consent and we will under no circumstances accept parental signatures as a substitute. We will not take revenge couples, or those who want to die purely to spite each other. We will also never take anyone who we suspect to have intoxicated their partner. We are not monsters. I am not a monster.

My sister and I offer different death packages to our clients ranging from the mundane to the fabulous. Some customers are extremely particular. Our most fashionable choice is the Romeo and Juliet style death, but this comes at a substantial cost. For this package, we cater them with a small chapel room, a coffin, a sword and a bottle of poison. My sister told me once that she'd like to die in this scenario. Personally, I wouldn't like to die at all. Surely it's better to live forever.

———

Others prefer a Bonnie and Clyde style ambush, and for this we sort them out with a classic car and make a few calls to some friends who know their way around a loaded weapon. Then there are those who are less specific. Hanging is quick and relatively painless but nerve gas is the most peaceful way to go. These options are much less enjoyable for me but everyone deserves their choice.

We've found that a lot of women want their partner to be the one who ends their life. These infatuated girls insist that the last thing they want to see in this life is their boyfriend pointing a cold gun between their eyes. Generally men love this idea. The only problem is deciding what to do with them after their girlfriend is dead. Some guys solidify or try to run when they see their lover slumped on the stone floor with blood fanning out from their hair. In the early stages we let them go. Now it is a different story. They signed their life away to us. We can't let them leave. We owe it to the dead women.

Once we had a couple who wanted to pretend that they didn't know what they were getting themselves into. They completely lost it when I uncovered the blade. As I brought the axe down on her slender ivory neck, the woman's eyes were burst and bloodshot from screaming at me to stop. If it was to authenticate the scenario, she was pretty convincing. These little details are all part of the fun.

My sister has taken a while longer to get used to our lifestyle than I have. The pain in her eyes is evident as we drag the dead bodies down to the mortuary, but I know that in her little black heart she loves this as much as I do. She continues to struggle, observe and wash away the blood because she believes in this. I have never forced her into anything but I don't want to let her leave. I hate the possibility of her out there in the world, meeting someone and falling for everything the people we deal with here have fell for. In the end she may receive that Shakespearean death she so desires. And that, I can tell you, would be a tragedy.

Waiting

Fraser Bruce

The old man had been up for some time. Coming to his senses after another lingering daydream, he found himself seated in his chair. His case had been packed well in advance and sat by the door. He stared at it with quite some dread until finally the notion of another cup of tea won him over. He slowly rose and took short paces into the kitchen, choosing to avoid the aid of his stick, and leaned on the counter waiting for the kettle to boil.

The chime of the teaspoon against his favourite mug was a familiar and calming sound before the comforting sip of tea. He still couldn't get it to taste quite the same as Val's, though. Nonetheless, he sneaked in another spoonful of sugar that she would not have approved of, shaking his head in recognition of this mischievous act. This had been his second cup this morning. Normally Val and he enjoyed their morning brew from the large china teapot – a Golden Wedding anniversary gift. Now, the old man relied on one-cup teabags. Handy as they are – they're just not the same, he thought.

Most things in the kitchen would be rendered surplus to requirements at Rosebank. Treasured items would have to be left behind, like the china teapot and the many magnets that clung like memories to the endurable twenty year old fridge-freezer. The old man smiled faintly as he studied these souvenirs. Quite a collection, he thought. There's when Steve and Jean went to Rome. Oh, 'Milan', and one from… Vienna? No, Venice. There's even the leaning tower from Pisa. Andy and Susan's kangaroo and koala from Surfers Paradise. The Eiffel tower too. All places he regretted never having visited with Val. Ah, but there's souvenirs from York and Scarborough.

It was Val, of course, that had to persuade the old man to go on a bus trip to Scarborough, only the summer before last. He hated the idea of being trapped on a coach for hours with countless other geriatrics. It was the women he especially disliked. He always thought Val lowered herself to their level. Constant talk of 'weans and grandweans' and the tiresome moaning about everyone and everything. The bus ride itself didn't do much to alter the old man's negative expectations. The journey began with the constant bickering of the couple in front rowing over who got to enjoy which sandwich filling from their packed lunch. Then it was the high-pitched gent seated right behind the old man's better ear that caused the most irritation, offering an unnecessary running commentary on the trip's progress with his basic statistical analysis of every road-sign the bus passed. The old man remembered with some affection, the way Val rolled her eyes as this fellow reported that Penrith services were now just ten miles away, whilst loudly assuring his wife that she would be able to go the toilet within the next fifteen minutes so long as the driver maintained his current speed…

The old man allowed himself a grin as he remembered the look Val gave when he suggested they should break away from the tour and nip off to the nearest pub together. He knew he had to comply. It was *her* trip, after all. Now he thought of it, he couldn't clearly recall the last drink they actually shared together. Maybe a glass of wine with dinner somewhere? He sighed.

A few other mementos were scattered around the fridge door, but the old man's gaze was drawn down to the freezer which was littered with colourful letters and numbers. He hadn't dared adjust the formations that his two grandchildren had set these magnets in when they last visited.

The old man had just two grandchildren, Sophie and Grace, from his only son Andy and his Australian wife, Susan. They were planning to emigrate back to the Gold Coast but postponed the move when Val died.

They don't visit much now. Not without their granny Val there. She always pestered the old man to make more of an effort with his family. He loved to watch the girls play but just couldn't involve himself in their games. Maybe if they had been boys, he conceded to himself, then he might have tried to be more active.

Not that he didn't love the girls. They were both pretty and seemed well mannered. They had taken after their Australian mother with their blonde hair. The old man had even thought the younger child, Grace, had the same eyes as Val. However, he always suspected that Susan never particularly liked him, though he could never put his finger on what he might have done to upset her.

'Those Australians are a stubborn lot,' his old drinking buddy Tommy Miller had told him. The old man had stopped taking counsel from Miller and his cronies down at The Flying Fox. The Fox had once been an enjoyable and regular haunt. Val had always been fair and he never sneaked off to the pub when he shouldn't have. Nor did he ever break his curfew by arriving home too late. Well, it was not so much a set curfew as it was more a mutual understanding between him and Val. Should the old man ever appear in an inebriated state, he always sought redemption in some form or another, typically by making Val breakfast the following morning - if he was fit. In recent years the old man had significantly cut back on his drinking habits, he had to. He hadn't even ventured to The Fox since the wake.

Turning to rinse his cup, the old man's attention was drawn to the window-sill behind the sink. He filled his empty mug with cold water and generously poured it over the ever present spider-plant that nestled there. Again, he drew a rather pained smile at the object but afforded himself a little chuckle. He had bought, well, acquired the plant on the day of Val's 70th birthday. His wife despised it, its spiky leaves and even the ugly grey pot the old man had placed it in. Hideous, she said. Hideous. The old man, in spite of this, had maintained and watered the plant for some nine years. Whilst Tommy Miller would always boast of his past infidelity, and others at The Fox bragged of their drinking and fighting conquests, the old man's only notable act of rebellion had been tending this spider-plant.

Will they have spider-plants at Rosebank?

He struggled back towards the living room – his feet shuffling and scuffing along the carpet, his balance unsteady. The strain on the old man's shoulders weighed him down and he slumped into his seat, releasing a long exhalation.

He panned the room. It was spacious, but everything in the house seemed to be watching him, judging him and now closing in on him. Pictures on the wall stared back. He was no longer at ease in his own home. No longer in control.

Val's empty chair sat opposite. He still couldn't bear to touch the seat, and scarcely could he even look at it before his pale eyes would begin to water. Yet through his blurred vision he would briefly, all too briefly, see the outline of his Val sitting contently with her hands clasped. When the old man wiped his eyes, the mirage would escape him.

Bowing his head, he became more conscious now of time. He knew, later this morning, Andy was coming to pick him up and take him to Rosebank. He heard every tick of the grandfather clock that had been passed down through Val's family. He felt the beats resonate with his own faltering heart-rate, every measured click of the clock's swinging hand chipping away at him. The stroke of every new passing second seemed to reinforce the years of opportunity that were now lost.

The old man would just become another statistic in a home.

He was waiting. Waiting for Andy.

Waiting to leave his house. Waiting.

Waiting for her.

Tread

Catherine Baird

———

Your right foot goes down first and you feel the slight squishing of the crêpey rubber soles
//// on your boots and imagine how high you are in comparison with the ceiling of the
//////// kitchen which is just through the wall to your left – each alternate step left or right
/////////// creates the same squishing which you may not get with other footwear, and
//////////////// although you cannot detect on a daily basis the wear on the carpet, you
/////////////////// know it is happening and regret each step because you know that your
////////////////////// movement day after day after day, up and down, down and up, tells
/////////////////////////// you that eventually the currently indecipherable ruin of the
//////////////////////////// carpet means you will have to buy a new one and although
//////////////////////////////// you have some money saved and already know that you
/////////////////////////////////// would choose a darker, more hard-wearing floor-
// covering the next time, the idea of moving the
// ironing board and the chest of drawers from
/// the top landing and all of the attendant
/// upheaval that will be caused is too
// much to be bothered with, so maybe
/// staying upstairs or downstairs
// forever is the only option.

Laughing Gulls

Julie Shennan

———

Joe looked at Alec, had he heard? Gusts of wind stung their ears, stunting conversation. Bands of rain collided into them. He hoped he had, he didn't want to say it again. Joe's outstretched hand was getting soaked, the envelope floppy. Finally, Alec took it. He opened it. There was no money, just a letter. The words 'regret' and 'redundancy' popped out of the page. Globs landed on it, running the ink. The impression stuck. As of tomorrow he had no work. This month's pay would be the last. A wave of panic surged from his chest to feet. He curled his toes, snatching for grip.

'You'll be okay, right?'

'Think so?'

'Sure. Something'll come up.'

Alec considered yelling, getting on his knees to beg but the ground was wet and he had never been one for words. His throat tightened and eyes stung. Indigestible frustration pushed a tear down his face. Its momentary warmth was erased by cold rain. He stuffed the letter in his pocket.

Leaning over, Joe clapped Alec on the back in a macho attempt at a hug. His frame jutted out, unused to the stance. The unexpected contact jerked Alec from his daze and he found himself patting the man's back in return. They blinked, moving away embarrassed. Joe turned and headed back up the street to his heated Merc and job security. He turned to look back at Alec. The poor guy's coat didn't even have a hood.

Alec didn't know where he was going. Following his boss seemed stupid, even if their cars were parked on the same street. He walked the opposite way up to the Clyde front. Rain and tears blurred his view, like trying to decipher an oil painting. Fairy lights smudged through the picture. Christmas was coming. Folded catalogue pages haunted him. Clothes and hair straighteners for Jen, a mobile phone for Lucy... What did an eight year old need a mobile phone for? He shook this excuse out his head. She deserved a decent Christmas.

Guilt turned his stomach like a cement mixer. It was his fault. He should have saved, it was what Dads did. His phone vibrated in his pocket: Jen wondering where he was. Alec stopped at the Clyde Bridge, looking over the side. His eye travelled the length of the canal, black water slugged along, bordered by grey banks and buildings. Gulls laughed overhead and rain spat in his face. His mind wandered to his kitchen work top, to the stacks of unpaid bills: gas, electric, broadband, life insurance. Alec bit his lip.

Shakily he slung one leg over the barrier, then the next. His hands clamped onto the chunky stone, rain drummed onto them. White streetlight gathered in the pools between his knuckles. His feet shook on the ledge. Water moved sluggishly beneath him, a narrow strip of footing separated him from its mass. He rocked forward pushing his chest out. Panic seized. His hands tightened. Pulse rushed. The phone vibrated again. Startled, almost loosening his grip. He wrenched back.

The phone escaped his pocket. Its blue screen flashed, falling. Plunging into the water, it illuminated murkiness and then nothing. Jen would be worried. He imagined her listening as the dial tone stopped, pacing the kitchen, looking at the clock, snapping at the weans. He squeezed his eyes shut, tried again, but couldn't let go. Brash voices sounded in the distance, probably teenagers. He couldn't be seen like this. Shuddering, he maneuvered himself back over the railing.

Alec turned his key, holding his breath. He could hear the TV. Hoped Jen was asleep. The door squeaked treacherously. It was pointless. She shot up from the couch, hair disheveled. Alec noted Lucy asleep on the other, her face peaceful, blanket kicked off. He stepped over to fix it. Jen blocked his way.

'Where the fuck have you been?'

'I just...'

'You just what?'

She hissed accusations of what he had 'just' been doing. Alec waited for her to stop. She didn't.

'There.'

He thrust the letter at her and slumped down on the coach. A blanket lay furrowed beneath him. He was dripping all over it. Jen read. The TV droned and Lucy snored softly. She looked up, throwing the letter back at him and nodding.

'Aye, you might as well get comfy.'

She slammed the living room door behind her, forgetting about Lucy.

One Seventy-Five into the Town, Mate

Cameron Steel

WELCOME TO GLASGOW, a dear green place. Tues 9am, good time for a bus? No! Buses transform into bingo hearses carrying pensioner's coins to Mecca. The Quay to last giddy thrill before death's chill. To thee only we worship.

Hanging on to these ropes... I Tarzan. Global Video-war, fairy tales, Cafe India, bookies, estate agents – climb that ladder! Window cleaner.

Movement at last. Departure at A.M. Buchanan. Memorials, sit down and relax in peace. Shafts of light, sun through the railings mock the pupils. Pillars of light, cloud and fire.

15 people, though the sign boasts 27. One is sat on the left hand seat, three back from the front. Square-jawed, all thumbs and sausages on the motorola. Two twittering girls are perched. A tall drip of a boy, a nerve with eyes, sits quietly determined to burst his eardrums. There is a man, there on that seat, drowning in his thoughts. A mother and her lamb, sit in front, no shepherd. PUSH BUTTON TO STOP.

From behind, rattling and rolling. Ah! A distinctive odour hangs and swims in the old ladies nets. The smell swaggers to the front and has a severe disagreement with the driver. Helen Street, streets behind. Too late as usual. *Right you two* he barks up the bus. *Wit, we wernae smokin.* Yes they were. *Aye, Aye, get yer stuff and get aff the bus.* Crossed tattoos, arms like legs. This is ma bus and you dae iz a say.

People observe the scene, with eyes and backs of heads or ears. The game is over: *AFF THE BUS!* The tangerine babbles and her partner stays silent. The praying mantis. One small step... and the bus offloads her terrible cancer. It withdraws and the windows wave at Buzz and Neil – they make one last defiant gesture: the fingers, not Churchill's. The bus picks up speed, she has forgotten to turn her oven off. Playing chicken with the traffic and tig wae the buses. The blue rinse brigade get off too at Mecca, to thee only do we worship. Harry Ramsdens: QUIZ NIGHT WITH HOST, fish chips and mushy questions.

The final stretch and into the heart of things. To do. The joy of pushing the button makes the lamb bleat. The twittering girls depart. Beauty dressing and hair therapy. He puts his sausages in his pocket and leaves, followed by the man with blood dripping from his ears.

Torn Cement (A Lipogram)

Martin Schauss

———

He explored the geometry of the block, hoped to resolve the problem. The concrete body, however, other to look so, never proved correct. On the cement blocks, he stood foot wobbly, tooth crooked. Not one corner showed coherence, not one block went down even. He felt doomed by the geometry. He threw bowels on the street. Movement seemed no longer the concern, lots of blocks, not one decent or correct. Cement below the foot, between the teeth, he tore the loose stones from broken corners to throw on the observers. They try to flee, so they fell over crooked cobblestones or blocks of wrong degrees onto clogged grooves. Clothes torn, they swore, condemned the person who wronged them.

He looked on, on to the torn vectors of the concrete blocks, never coherent, never correct to the forms of geometry he so longed for. The correct corners of the owned room he termed home tempted to flee the deformed concrete scene. He lost one tooth, looked to the tooth on the cement down next to the foot. He tore one other tooth off the rotten flesh, threw the tooth down. The two teeth on the cement, he felt the bowels tremble. He no longer bore the concrete blocks, the wrong geometry, the crooked corners.

On one he tore the self from the perverted world. He felt the proper concord of new, reverted to the old room, remote from the torn cement beyond the front door.

The Pilish City

Martin Schauss

———

Saw a city,
a
block construct of cement
teeth.
The block geometry, incorrect crooked
construct, was an odd criminal form. Vector to vector,
over the
mad calculus and in unsound buildings,
moved on shocking concrete grit.
A landscape invalid,
I reason, irregular and illogical,
imperfect. The strange angle I would exorcise of
conscious reality. Life, mechanism with grit teeth, defective in
the rotting geometry, I shield from angles
in calculus errors or criminal revolting cityscape. Creating absurd
as negative for
grit scraping
on edges, add
core of incoherence. Figures, digits, numbers corrupted. Everyone
is a lost database,
obsolete, caught tired. I run in
erroneous as
mad cycles...

The Script

Simon Cassidy

———

'Mr. Copeland...'

'Please, call me Lance.'

'Eh, sorry... Lance... the script, it's just not that funny.'

'Oh?'

'I mean... the characters are fine, and the plot seems... OK... but overall... I just...'

'You just what, Tom?'

'I don't think its quite ready for filming yet... needs a bit of work...'

'Define "a bit of work"?'

Burying his face in his hands, Tom let out a long sigh. This was their third session, and so far, there had been little progress.

'Tom, I know you are the writer, but I think I am the one with experience here. I know what makes a show work, and the Network loves it.'

Lance sat, his elbow hooked over the back of his chair with one leg slung over the other; a half smile hovering about the lips of his sharp features. Tom looked at his partner. He was wearing skinny jeans, a frilled shirt and pointed shoes. They may have been designer, but they didn't have the desired effect.

'It reminds me of when I was on Broadway with Nathan Lane...'

The Network, Tom was well aware, did not love it. Had they loved it, he would not be sitting in his humid, airless office on a Saturday afternoon with a motionless smile on his face. He tried to feign interest as he listened to the endless success stories.

***

It was only a week ago that Ray Layfield, the booming, swaggering Texan and the head of Impact Network, came striding into Tom's office, wearing his usual Stetson, boots and impeccably cut grey suit: 'Tim!' he began, sitting on the desk 'this is your lucky day!'

Tom was a writer... or at least he tried to be. His day job didn't allow much room for creativity. He was a transcriptionist; fancy title, but in essence a gopher. He spent his working day listening to other people talk in meetings, and then transcribing his notes so that everyone above him looked good. He had been promised 'advancement opportunities' and 'hands-on experience at the ground level'. He had written an occasional scene when no one else was interested, and had once made a coffee for Tom Cruise, but even that was six years ago.

'Oh, hello Mr Layfield,' Tom began. 'What can I do for you?'

'Tim, Tim, Tim! Just call me Ray.'

He choked back an impulse to call him Roy and stammered 'OK... Ray. What can I do for you?'

'You're thinking, I'm a writer. You're wonderin' why the hell we're keeping you at transcript when all you really want to do is get those creative juices flowing, am I right?'

He did not wait for a reply.

'Well son, I got a new show comin' up, and I think it would be the perfect opportunity for you to step up and get involved. Up to the task?'

'Yes of course,' Tom replied quickly.

'That's the spirit. Over the last few weeks we have been in very quiet talks with the agent of a certain Mr Lance Copeland.' He paused.

'Anyway, he's decided that he wants to take a more backstage role; guess he's gotten a little fed up with the limelight. He's written a screenplay for a mini series, pure comic gold we've been told, and naturally we don't want any other networks pickin' up on it, so we grabbed it without thinking twice.'

Ray frowned and leaned forward.

'Now obviously we have every faith in Lance, but you know, our Network has a reputation to live up to, and we need Lance's show to reflect that. So, when you're working with him, it's important you remember that.' With that, he clapped him on the back and said, 'I'm sure you will do just fine, sport!'

Tom closed the apartment door. He guessed from the clinking and rustling sounds coming from the kitchen, that Tara was preparing dinner.

'Hey Babe, good day?' he asked, taking a beer from the fridge. 'Boss came and spoke to me today personally. Looks like I'm finally getting involved in a show, brand new series. Isn't that great? Told ya if I kept working hard it would pay off... eventually.

'And I've not even told you the best part yet,' he said, attempting to give her a quick kiss, before squeezing himself into the chair behind the small kitchen table. 'It's written by Lance Copeland, *the* Lance Copeland. If it's a hit, might even mean we can think about moving...'

***

Tom walked through the plush lobby of the Hilton, adjusting his jacket and checking his watch. He looked up as a portly Englishman approached him,

'Hi Tom. Glad you could make it. My name is Sam, Lance's agent.' He clasped Tom's hand with both of his and shook it vigorously 'Hungry?'

They ordered food and exchanged small talk, before turning the conversation to the script.

'So,' Sam asked, 'Have you read it? Lance is really excited to have you on board.'

'Oh... Thanks.' Tom said, a little confused by the statement 'Yes... yes of course I've read it.' Tom replied.

'Excellent. Really exciting don't you think? Lance can't wait to get cracking with it.'

'Me neither, it is a real privilege to be working with him.'

'Good. Would you like some wine? Any preference?'

'It's a bit early in the day for me, but please, you go ahead.'

'I think I will.' Taking a large drink from his glass, Sam turned his attention back to Tom. 'What did you think of it? The script I mean.'

'The script, yes. I... the music is really good.'

'I know,' he grinned.

'Yeah...' Tom conceded, 'but to be honest I think the overall script needs some work.'

Sam leaned forward in his chair, clasping his hands on the table in front of him; his eyebrows furrowing as he listened to Tom talk through the script, outlining some of his suggestions. '...it's just more in keeping with the tone of the Network that way, you know?'

Sam straightened slightly, leaned forward to refill his glass and looked across at Tom. 'You certainly seem to have given this some thought,' he said. 'However, I think I need to straighten you out on one or two things, just before you get carried away with yourself. Now, I'll concede, that in places the script... *might* need some minor adjustments but that's *your* job; to iron out the niggling little details. Not to overhaul the whole show into some primetime drivel.'

'Let me explain something else to you,' he said raising his voice, 'your Network is just one of many we were offered. Make no mistake about it, Lance equals big money for your station and if you don't change your attitude, I will call your superiors and take our project elsewhere. Are we clear?'

***

'You know, I really believed this was my chance,' he told Tara, sitting at his kitchen table, absently peeling the label off the now tepid beer. 'Really thought they had finally given me a break. Ten years, ten fucking years and this is my big break?' He laughed, leaned back and stared up at the roof of their small, cramped kitchen. 'I can't change the script without pissing off Sam; and if I don't change the script, Ray is going to fire me.'

'Mmm, are you finished with that?' Tara said, glancing over her shoulder at the half eaten chicken on his plate.

'Maybe it will be OK,' Tom said finally, his voice cracking slightly. 'Next week I get to work with Lance, one on one, no distractions; maybe I can talk him round, it's his show after all, right?'

***

This was the third meeting.

'It reminds me of the time I was on Broadway...'

Tom sat at the desk, with his head resting on his hand, nodding politely and trying to feign interest in Lance's story. Laughing at his own jokes, name dropping at every opportunity, Lance didn't notice. Tom felt his left leg twitching spasmodically and realised that he was chewing frustratedly at the end of his pen.

'I understand that Lance,' he began.

'You should have been there Tom.' Lance continued.

'Lance...this isn't Broadway... the Network... Lance.' Tom's voice began to waver. The twitching in his leg grew faster and his knuckles white, as they clenched his pen.

'It's all about compromise Tom,' Lance was saying, 'and just like you, I was reluctant...' His voice faded as Tom fought to maintain his composure. 'Lance... but... this is my job... Lance.'

The pen cracked between Tom's teeth as he ground them together, staring at the unconcerned, babbling form of Lance Copeland.

' ...and I'm sure you remember how that turned out Tom,' Lance said. 'It just shows, you should always be willing to listen.'

Tom dropped his pen on the desk, touching one thumb to his mouth to remove the ink that stained his lip. With a sigh, Tom raised his eyes and looked directly at Lance. This was his dream, Tom reminded himself. He flexed his fingers, took a deep breath and tried to relax. It can still work, he thought, it damn well has to.

'OK Lance,' he said, running his hands slowly down his face, 'Let's start from the beginning... '

Reasonable Doubt

Matthew Lynas

——

Well aye we were at the pub so we wur
both a bit drunk.
No legless or anythin,
we didnae have any trouble getting served.
I was out wae three mates.
Aye, Mr Russell, Mr Johnston and Mr Kane.
Ah hud met hur once before that night,
it wis at a flat warmin party,
she was there wae her boyfriend.
I don't really mind much
about that night though.
To the best of ma ability?
Well we only talked for a wee bit,
like I said I didnae know her that well.
I think that's why she came oer
to me in the pub though.
Aye she had been drinking
and came over to chat.
We ended up dancing,
I didn't think anything of it
cos ae her boyfriend
you know.
He wisnae there though
she said she was just out
wae a couple a girls fae work.
About midnight her pals
went tae get the last train but
she said she was stayin out.
I said she could stay at mine
if she wanted
or we'd chip in a bit for her taxi
or somethin

It was just me and two girls from work.
We went over this in my statement.
OK. Miss McKeown and Miss Brown.
We weren't planning on staying
long. Just out for a few.
We went to the bathroom together
and that's when I saw
him.
I said hello as I walked past.
When we came back to the table we
finished our drinks before going
to the bar.
That's when I started feeling
funny.
Well yes strange. I wouldn't say
sick. Dizzy I guess. Miss McKeown
was ordering a drink and I leaned
against a stool at the bar.
I was hunched over.
I don't know why they didn't take
me home. Insist? I don't think they
could insist.
I'd never been out with them before.
Well you'll have to ask them. I
guess they thought I was just a
lightweight. Having too much of
a good time. Maybe if they had...
I'm sorry can we stop for a minute?

Shots, she wanted to do shots
I'm not really intae that
but
we were having a good time

We were dancing, sort of.
He said that? I don't remember
wanting anything to drink. I don't really
remember much at all

so
I decided to just go along wae it.
Was I trying tae wit?
Aye it would be fair to say
Ah found her attractive.
She said it wus me that kissed her?
Well mibbie, I don't mind dancing
that well. We got sortie caught up.
Shots, dancing, it was dark and loud
and then we were sort of kissin.
Fine, yes we were kissin.
Aye next tae the big speakers
the ones at the back ae the dancefloor,
Ah think that's why they left.
Aye Mr Russell, Mr Johnston and Mr Kane.
They did send me a text.
Can I read it?
Awrite, it said 'Well in
big man.'
Well we went outside and waited
fur a taxi outside the chip shop.
Well if I wis on ma own ad huv walked.
Naw I don't think it would be
fair to say she wis unsure.
I know she text hur mum tae
say she was staying at a friend's.
Well that's wit she telt me.
If the taxi driver is here I know
he'll tell yae that we wur kissin
in the back seat
Aye a put my hand on hur leg
but when she said stope a stopped.
I think it wis more to do wae us
bein in the taxi more than anyhin else.
Got a little carried away?
Naw, no really.
Aye she had no problem wae coming upstairs
she even asked if I hud any more drink.
I still hud a half bottle a vodka fae a party
last week. We listened tae some music
Here wits the point in this?
Look a didnae try anything she wasn't
inviting. We started kissin again and we

except for spinning and feeling
nauseous. I wanted to get out.
He put his arms over my shoulder,
I looked at his two friends and they
sort of laughed and left.
It was just me and him in the place
and that's when I started to feel sick
and pretty tired.

Maybe it was the chipshop I don't know
I was too busy trying to text my mum.
I wanted to go home but I couldn't.
Look you don't understand
I tried to text her, I even closed one
eye to look at the screen but it
was all blurry.

He kept forcing himself on top of me
in the taxi. No he didn't attempt
penetration. But still.
I just sort of pushed him away.
My head was hurting and I could
hardly keep my eyes open.
He was touching me and the
taxi driver didn't say a thing.
I was trying to say something but I
could only groan.
I don't really remember much until his
bedroom.
Why? Because there are some parts
that are more important than others.
I remember feeling afraid. Not knowing
where I was. Have I been back to the house

moved intae the bedroom. Things were awrite
and then she pure freaked out. Why? A dunno
do ah? Started shouting at me and ran out.
I didnae chase after her and I didnae force her
to do
Anyhin
How the fuck should a know?
She just went pure mental.
Aye well mibbie she did feel like that but
Look am telling yae a did fuck all.

since? Yes, we had to go with the police.
Look he brought me into his
bedroom and I could hardly stand up.
I tried to tell him, tried to push him
but I felt so dizzy, so tired. I just gave up

he wouldn't stop,
he just kept going.
It wasn't me, there was nothing I could
do. When I woke up I was outside.
lying by a bus stop.
I don't know how I got. I'm sorry can we
stop for a minute it's just.
Look I've done nothing wrong here. Why
would I make this up?

On Tour

Charlene Moore

Patrick was surprised that the bouncers let him and the lads inside. Barry had warned them all before they'd set off that Storm was exclusive as fuck, and the bouncers were gorillas in tuxedos: lunatics who'd sooner give you a fist in the gut than escort you inside. But the gorillas must have been feeling docile tonight: they barely grunted before unclipping the black velvet rope which blocked off the club doors. The lads strode through with cocky swagger, acting like they couldn't give a fuck either way, all five hearts banging like mad in case the bouncers changed their minds.

'Well fucking done, mate,' said Jonathan, when he guessed that they were far enough away. Patrick smiled smugly. He couldn't wait to text Barry to tell him that he'd gotten the lads into Storm. Barry was his best mate in Glasgow, but even Patrick admitted that he was an annoying shite: one of those smug pricks that had turned DJing at high school discos into a career, had a gorgeous girlfriend who adored him, and a different fit bird falling out of his bed every weekend. But Barry wasn't here tonight, couldn't make it because of work in Glasgow, and that meant Patrick was in charge.

The others lads – Jonathan, Callum, Scott and Andy – had nominated Patrick because they thought he'd have the best chance of getting them into the club. Patrick was It, and all the lads knew it, even if they would never admit it out loud. He had thick black hair, full lips and dark blue eyes. Girls fell into them and disappeared without ever being seen again. As if all of that wasn't enough, he also had a soft Irish accent after living in Cork for a bit as a kid. Even if the bouncers hadn't fancied letting the group in, one look at Patrick would have changed their minds: where Patrick went, the stiffening of nipples followed.

Tonight was all about finding the right nipples. The lads had heard that Storm was the place where all the hottest birds in London partied. Jonathan and Scott both had girlfriends, but they all wanted to pull a London bird. Preferably one with the face of Alexa Chung and the tits of Danielle Lloyd. Patrick probably had the best chance of finding this girl. Storm was one of those places where the music is turned up full blast to stifle conversation, but that didn't matter. Patrick wanted a girl with the tits of Danielle Lloyd – no one mentioned having to talk to her.

It was absolutely heaving. Patrick didn't think he'd ever seen so much skin in his life. At the union back home girls would come to the bar straight after lectures, dressed down in tight jeans and vest tops, showing off slim legs and a hint of cleavage. In Storm they flitted past like exotic butterflies; he couldn't see a single pair of jeans or vest top, instead hundreds of girls danced against each other in low cut tops and skirts that barely covered their arse cheeks. Patrick wasn't complaining: he just felt slightly indecent, and a little hard, squeezing through the throngs of sweaty, semi-naked clubbers on his way to get a drink.

Callum chose their place at the bar. He tried to pretend it was because it was the quietest place he could see, even though they all knew it was because of the knot of girls standing close by. Callum had a thing for fat chicks. He never said so, but the lads had seen the porkers he had pulled on the last few nights out. He'd actually gotten away with it too: 'Fat girls will do *anything*,' Jonathan had insisted, while the others nodded along. Jonathan had never pulled a girl bigger than a size 12, but he was still considered the authority on fatties. Patrick didn't like fat chicks: big tits were one thing, but a big arse was quite another. He ignored the girls Callum had his eye on, and leaned over the bar.

* * *

After five White Russians, four vodka and cokes, two pints of Snakebite and half an E, Patrick finally decided to bless the chubby girls with his conversational wit. He was well oiled, one arm slung over the shoulder of the girl nearest him, his hand swaying precariously near her breasts. He yelled over the music to tell them about the time Scott was caught shagging a bird old enough to be his mum: 'And there he was, right, jeans round his ankles, behind her, with a stiffie big enough to harpoon Moby Dick!' The girls screamed with laughter; silent howls swallowed up by the pounding bass of the dance track. He glanced at the girl under his arm, she was alright, Patrick thought: straight blonde hair, a wide smile and a deep cleavage. He noticed a round red and yellow *18 Today* badge pinned to her top, right next to her pillowy breasts. He stared down and slurred more of the lad's sexploits, and the girls shook with laughter: delighting in the delicious horror of it all.

Then, ignoring the smashed laughter, a new girl squeezed through. Sadly for the birthday girl – who had hoped that, after downing his sixth White Russian, Patrick might have copped off with her – while Alexa or Danielle might not have made it to Storm that night, Patrick wanted to do all the same things to this one. She sashayed through the crowd with a tiny waist and long chocolate brown waves; leaned over the bar in front of Patrick, her snug red dress riding up over tanned thighs, and yelled a drinks order at the barman. She'd definitely done that deliberately – out of the entire bar, why else would she choose there unless she was trying to seduce him? She got served quickly, of course, and turned back round to face the club. Patrick would have liked to step towards her, but reckoned he was safer anchored to fatty. Despite being propped up by another female, the girl smiled at Patrick. With a face like that she knew he'd be a heartbreaker. She had an appetite for trouble: she loved it, lived it, was it. She kept smiling and stepped towards him.

Patrick had met his London bird, and she was the stuff of wet dreams. He was already bragging to Barry in his head when the 1 and the 8 on the birthday girl's badge began to

swim

and wane,

the red and yellow

bleeding together. No one else seemed to have noticed

yet
though. The girl in the red dress yelled
'How's

your

night been
so

far then?'

Patrick clenched the edge of the bar with a sweaty palm, and the
boom,

boom,

boom,
of the music began to echo, reverberating through his brain. He slipped away,
away from his London bird,

past snatches
of echoed conversation
which flowed together like

hundreds

of tape-recorders running
simultaneously.
He forced himself

forward,
stumbling through

the sweaty shoulders,

the short skirts,

the happy little faces,

of oblivious clubbers,

trying to find the cool safety of the

toilets.

'Patrick?

Is that you in there,

you fucking idiot?'

Callum laughed.

'You are such a fucking steamboat, man – I've been looking for you for fucking ages. Come on out.' Patrick heard his friend stagger against the cubicle door and laugh. Where he was – the smooth black marble of the tiles, the white porcelain cistern, the skinny roll of toilet paper – came hurtling towards him like he'd been shot through a tunnel. He pushed up from the floor on weak legs, and urged his heart to

slow down, slow down, slow down.

His head was pounding and his throat burnt raw. There was vomit in the toilet bowl, splashed on the seat, and smeared down his shirt in smelly finger streaks. It was off-white, like sour milk. 'I'll get you back out there,' Andy said, 'I'm well in there with that blonde lassie. That stunner you blew off is well gone, mate, you stupid prick. Hurry up though, for fuck sake. There's still time for another couple before we're booted out.'

Patrick swung open the unlocked cubicle door. He could hear the muffled dance music which squeezed through the toilet door from the club. He was alone except for one other man by the urinals – dick in hand, trying to aim a stream of piss, while his entire body swayed and staggered, head lolling back. He turned when he heard Patrick come out of the cubicle, 'Alright mate?' piss spraying up the wall.

Patrick stared at himself in the mirror. Thick black hair, full lips scabbed with sick and dark blue bloodshot eyes. Girls fell into them and disappeared without ever being seen again. Patrick wiped his mouth with wet toilet roll to wash off the crust of vomit. He already knew that when he got back to Glasgow he'd tell his mates that he met a girl with the face of Alexa Chung and the tits of Danielle Lloyd. She'd taken him back to her flat, and sat on his face. London was fucking incredible. Patrick was It.

Bottles

Gabriella Bennett

Of varying heights and widths, like Christmas carol singers on a door-step, five empty bottles stand together in the background of a still life composition to provide perspective to the other objects in the painting. The small squat bottle in the corner wonders silently why it isn't important enough to be talked about – instead, it is only the milk it held that ever got any attention. It once contained the liquid that nourished a baby when its mother couldn't breastfeed – it saved the infant. It can barely be seen next to the sensual colours of fruit and cloth. Similarly, the dull plastic medicine bottle laments the loss of its tablets that ended the days of a man. Who would want to hear the story of what is now just a shell over the zesty musings of love? The see-through structures cannot help but reflect the things around them and are frustrated that they are not appreciated in their own right. While they sit and sigh, the artist aligns their conventionally linear forms, so easily represented by a brush stroke, in order to frame everything else that would be lost without the almost invisible outline of form.

The Carpenter

Katrina Patrick

He walked the beach as the sun was rising.
His eyes would crinkle against the wind,
And search the shoreline for driftwood
As pebbles from foreign places
Chatter amicably with his boots.

They would tell the old leather of mountain streams
Flush and dancing with melted snow
And the old leather would boast to them
Of sunsets on long country roads
And the rush of wheat fields in summer.

The tales and memories ended at his ankles
For his boot buckles were newly cast
And could not remember
The bright fires of the forge
Or the quarry before it.

The carpenter himself could tell the best stories of all
But he held no time for the past
And his boots had long since given up
Reminding him of his wife
Or the war that took her from him.

Some things were better left to boots
And the eager pride of prattling shingle.

Born Free

Marianne Gallagher

———

According to those that know, the 'Wee Rovers' are the worst team in Scotland. Although they are no strangers to the bottom end of the littlest league, they are not seen as failures – in fact they are regarded with universal affection, cherished for their persistence and the manner in which they never lose hope. Of all the underdogs, they are most loved and tenacious. Perhaps this was what was on Kevin Williamson's mind when he fielded his team of rookie players 15 years ago.

Children of Albion Rovers, the first anthology to come from the Rebel Inc. imprint, collected the work of a seminal group of writers together for the first time, to create a landscape of a new literary Scotland. Bringing together the writing talent of Irvine Welsh, Alan Warner, Gordon Legge, James Meek, Laura Hird and Paul Reekie, it capitalised on the growing scene in Edinburgh and spoke to people in voices that they recognised, about things they experienced themselves. It broke with tradition, eschewing the cosy landscapes of the literature that went before, and celebrated the vernacular and the filth of urban Scottish life – both looking for the light inbetween the cracks and examining the darkness.

Rebel Inc. itself began life as a literary magazine. Inspired by the punk fanzines of the 1970's which celebrated their D.I.Y. ethic and challenged the status quo of the conventional music press, Williamson aimed to take a 'sledgehammer to the literary establishment.' This counter-cultural journal wanted a place to express the frustrations of a country post-Thatcher, and examine the raved-up and raved-out landscape of Scotland in the 90s. For 4 years it ran, staying true to its mantra of 'fuck the mainstream!' with the publication of 1994's 'Ecstasy Interview' which recorded an unedited conversation between Irvine Welsh and Kevin Williamson whilst both were under the influence of the drug MDMA. This, somewhat understandably, brought massive attention to the magazine – both dismissive and approving – and marked it out as a challenging, provocative publication.

But notoriety aside, the focus at Rebel Inc. was always on the writing. When Trainspotting (excerpts from which featured in the virgin issue of the journal) hit the big-time, Williamson felt that the magazine had lost its underground edge and thought it better to steer the work into a book format. This was a response to the London-centric publishing world, and the needs of a Scottish movement to find their home and express their voice. Rebel Inc. began to publish through Canongate, and the *Children of Albion Rovers* were born.

Opening with Kevin Williamson's pseudo-team talk as he guides us through the strengths, skills and tactics of each individual player, *Albion Rovers* takes the footballing theme into its subject matter and its vocabulary; particularly in Welsh's study of sci-fi casuals, 'The Rosewell Incident'. There is even a set of football cards, originally given away with copies of *The List*. Although football is on the menu, it is far from limited in its scope – from the story of sexually calculating schoolgirls in Hird's 'The Dilating Pupil' to the acid-baked adventures of Oban ravers offered by Alan Warner's 'After the Vision', themes of humour and realism are universal.

Published in the same year as *Trainspotting*, the anthology was destined for cult success. The influence of Irvine Welsh and the subsequent popularity of Scottish literature enabled the 'Rovers' to pack out night-club readings and perform alongside Lou Reed at The Hague. For a time, owning a copy of the anthology was like owning a copy of an out-of-print, legendary record – it was like a pass to a special club, where everyone was cool and literary but street-smart to boot. They were equally well-versed in literature as they were fluent in the language of the real and the ordinary. It was a riposte to the snobbery of the literary critics, who were bowled over by this raw and real portrayal of life on the other side.

In the press, the group were touted as the 'Edinburgh beats'. A combination of clever writing and very clever marketing turned the book into a phenomenon, and its philosophy into a brand. Gimmicks aside, the writing remains as strong as it did in 1996. The concerns of the 90s are high on the agenda, from the television shows name-checked to the 'Wonderwall' lyrics which adorn its pages. Whilst it is a piece which is distinctively of its time and place, the essential freshness and vitality of the language retains its power, despite the aging of some of its references.

Gordon Legge brought the pop writing, Irvine Welsh the whack of reputation and the schemie slang. Laura Hird gave a tale of a teen Lolita and an aging, ogling teacher. From Meek, one of the more underrated gems of the collection – the scheming and misbehaviour of Edinburgh traffic wardens was brought into sharp focus, by way of a new uniform and a Chinese board game. Alan Warner brought the hallucinogens and the hallucinogenic imagery – lest we forget that we are in the grip of the 'Chemical Generation'. Strong pieces in a strong collection.

'Submission' by Paul Reekie is the stand-out novella here, combining high-brow literary allusions with the humour and language of the terraces and the pub. Already a legendary figure on the spoken-word scene, we follow Reekie as he guides us through his punk rock teenage years to his grown-up misdemeanours – a journey through drugs, clubs, authors and records.

Written in the first person, it is presented as a work of fiction, yet it was the text which caused a radical revision of the entire anthology. A tabloid journalist – allegedly the basis for one of the characters in the book – took umbrage to its subject matter. The original edit was revoked, and a heavily censored version published in its place. Reekie responded to the allegations of his ex-wife claiming: 'All I've done, as any author does, is to arrange the facts to suit my purpose, which is to entertain.' And entertain it does, dredging up stories from the underground, shining light into previously unrecorded places with intelligence and gallows humour. The reading becomes more poignant when we learn of Reekie's suicide in June 2010; this brilliant, unpredictable novella the last published work of a brilliant and unpredictable man.

Following the reworking of *Submission* the anthology was rereleased, but things were not the same. Some of the heart had been edited out of it, and the legal wrangles were draining and difficult. Shortly after, the relationship between Canongate and Rebel Inc. faltered, and ties were severed. This golden moment in Scottish literature was over in name and publishing rights, but the spirit of the 'Albion Rovers' could be seen to live on. The collective continue to write and publish – from the multi-million selling Welsh to the more underground, subversive work of Laura Hird.

Although the alignment of music, film and thought saw the Rebel Inc. philosophy tied up in a movement, the real success – and intention – of the anthology was in opening up doors. The many literary events and readings which continue on and around Scotland are testament to the ethos of this original team. Rebel Inc. may have hung up its boots, but the ideas it brought to the game will continue to run and run.

Kyoto Blues
Martin Schauss

Kyoto town, nightly cool, tourists sleep, rest their feet,
Strangers to t'local rite jamming all nighttime through.
Sound-check done, guitar strums, bassist plucks, drummer hits,
Johnny sits inside his fav'rite bar list'ning hard.

Sweaty brows, fingers fast, rhythmic ride, voices thin,
Trucker caps, flashy shirts, coloured hair, baggy jeans,
Johnny loves yellow men playing straight US blues
ZZ Top, Stevie Ray, Jimi and BB King.

Kirin pint pleases him, nipping glad, sitting back,
Nippon chat, staring looks over to Johnny who
Never minds, never got native talk. Johnny comes
Only for Kyoto's folks playing sweet yellow blues.

A Villager

Martin Schauss

———

I cannot write about the Garden of Eden
Or the path from Bethlehem to Golgotha
I cannot write about a kiss from Desdemona
Or a dagger dangling in midair

I cannot write about the lakes in Cumbria
Or about the Caucasian mountains
Where rebels seek serenity and peace
Or fight a duel of honour on a precipice

I cannot write about the American Dream
Destroyed under everyone's very nose
About the vast freedom of Route 66
Which turned into the greatest joke of all

I can write about my old village
Its fifty-odd houses and church
I can write about its ninety-eight souls
That is if you don't count the cows

I can write about neighbours, write about dogs
Or cats and rats in the farmer's hay
Or indeed about the old farmer's family
Who built their ugly grange in the vale

I can write about the mad fat bitch
Who sprays pink paint on erring rabbits
And lets her basement to a racist cripple
Who shouts and screams on stormy nights

I can write about the adopted son
Living up the hill with his new mum
Who fled the village stoned out of his mind
To go straight behind bars in the big big world

In Threes

Craig Lamont

———

Our almost-instinct almost true:
what will survive of us is love.
                    Philip Larkin

After filling the silence with likely words, they were glad to get home to their ground-floor flat. On the way in Lewis noticed the curtains in the flat above were drawn. He was used to seeing Ethel there, perched on her window-sill like an old bird watching people come and go. Lewis sat down as soon as he got inside.

'*The natural order of things,* Lewis?' Rose said, standing over him.

'Aye, that's it. Out with the old and in with the new.'

'You do realise you're forty next year? And we've just buried my Aunt? How can you be so flippant?'

'We all mourn in our own ways. And right now I'm still thirty-nine... I'm not *there* yet,' he said, swivelling his finger around his temple and crossing his eyes.

This made her laugh, and Lewis felt himself smile. It was a shame he didn't realise laughter can't cure all ills. He remembered being at school, sitting next to the smart boy who would sneeze without covering his mouth. One day in Physics the teacher was telling Lewis off for doodling, and after humiliating him in front of the class she said: 'Are you listening? You'd better take heed.'

He stared at her for a second then put his hands on his head, assumed a puzzled expression and said, 'But miss, I've already got a heid.'

The next week when he was allowed back to his normal seat the smart boy said, 'Did you know that every time you laugh it adds a minute to your life?'

Lewis didn't know that, and did well pretending not to care. But ever since his diagnosis he wished for a life as simple as wasted laugher. Postponing your death and not knowing it means you never doubted living forever in the first place. This condition kept Lewis on the sharp edge of uncertainty. Sometimes he forgot all about it. Like when he watched Rose laugh, watched her eyes shrink with comfort, her smile unfold like expensive silk, he would remember his youth and hope the smart boy was as smart as everyone said he was.

Rose went to the kitchen. He listened to the water growl and the kettle click and he pictured vapours rolling in the air. He kicked off his shoes that he'd polished for the occasion. He rolled up his black tie, put it in the wardrobe till next time. Next time. It seemed sooner than comfort allowed. His thoughts grew from there and wandered off. *Shouldn't every closure be a kind of break? A Kit-Kat? A sweet release from unrelenting worry?* He imagined grasping a small ball of clay and for a second he felt the shape in his hand, instantly turning to dust. Ideas like this often settled in Lewis's mind. They were the most difficult things to get rid of, floating in the light and dancing in the shadows, presenting themselves when he was happy.

He heard the tea being poured. Rose's soft sniffing. When she came back to the couch she handed Lewis his mug without looking at him.

Lewis put the TV on. 'Do you miss her?' he asked as the adverts played out like someone's annoying, spoiled child.

She left the room and came back with a roll of toilet paper.

'If you want to talk I'm here.'

She blew her nose in response. It was a long weak sound like an amateur bugler practising in private. He wanted to grab her and shake her out of her grief. He wanted to remember some of the times Rose's Aunt was around, maybe a nice memory would cheer her up.

Lewis's reaction to Rose being upset was always a mechanical process. In the end he'd feel guilty, as if he'd personally done her wrong. It went like this:

Confusion: Why is she so upset? Does she not remember that time I made her breakfast? That time I made her laugh till she cried, what about that?

Denial: No chance. When did I say that? Is it like me to say that? I think I'd remember saying something like that, Rose.

Clarity: Oh, so I did. Shit.

The only word these processes could ever muster was a quiet, deflated, 'Sorry'. It took saying it to realise that he'd said it too much without knowing why, and then he'd forget and do it all again.

They'd been together since their teens, but the basics never changed. Sleeping on an argument didn't get easier with time. But Lewis didn't expect it to. When Rose lamented a lost earring, a broken vase, he didn't see the problem.

'There's your excuse to buy some new stuff,' he'd say with a happy shrug.

I'll give her time, Lewis thought, and went to the bathroom to shave. He used the same razor his dad left him. He'd always wanted an electric shaver, but Rose wouldn't allow it. She'd read once that they could affect people with Lewis's condition. He took off his bracelet and his thumb ring. He brought his hand to his face and studied his wedding band. The embossed decoration had faded considerably. A dull dark line wound round the gold ring. It might have been the stem of a flower. Now it was just a line. He tried to take it off, felt it tighten around his knuckle, and left it in place. As he slid the blade across his face, the sound of clean cutting. In between each cut, cut, cut, Rose's sobs could be heard.

*

As night came, Rose fell asleep on the couch, her fingers resting on her neck. Lewis went to hold her hand to wake her up. She stirred but didn't wake, and Lewis felt a little

jolt. He put the tips of his fingers to her throat and felt her pulse steadying. The subtle beat made him regret not having a child. The last time didn't work and they'd been putting off the topic since then. Being older, he took it for granted it was her decision whether or not to give up trying.

He felt for his own pulse and couldn't find it. When he did it was almost the same as Rose's, beating almost as naturally. He decided to see if their pulses were beating simultaneously. In feeling them both he heard them, and his face flushed with excitement. They seemed to be getting louder. For a second he thought of their pulses as independent beings and he was afraid he'd scare them off. He took her hand in his, and felt the faintest throbbing on the ridges of her fingertips.

A creak in the ceiling. A man coughed and spluttered violently. It was Donald from the flat upstairs, and there was a phone ringing. It seemed Donald just couldn't be bothered answering it, or getting an answering-machine. *It's amazing what technology can do. Save time, save lives.* The ceiling groaned as if Donald had just sat on the floor. When the phone eventually gave up, Lewis decided to turn in for the night. Rose's eyelids were flickering slightly. He got to his knees, put one arm under Rose's legs, put the other under her back, lifted her. When he walked to the bedroom he realised he hadn't carried her like this since their wedding night. It had started as a joke; their need to hate clichés.

She felt smaller in his arms. Maybe it was because she was sleeping, or because she was older now. He rocked her a bit, surprised at his strength, and placed her down on the bed. Feeling a pain in his chest he remembered he wasn't supposed to push his limits. After every operation he had to wait six weeks before playing football, going to the gym, lifting weights, or wives. Every five years he had to get a new battery fitted.

'See. Having a pacemaker's not that bad,' Rose once said as they left the hospital. 'You're my Duracell Bunny.'

He left the light off and undressed. The phone rang again, more distant and muffled now from this part of the flat.

Lying down, Lewis shut his eyes. It brought the ringing closer, like it was coming from their bedroom. He pictured the house upstairs: the curtains drawn, some candles lit. He was remembering the funeral they'd been to. The obedience of the ceremony, the smell of wood, the plain-faced priest...

...sleep came quickly but didn't last long. Rose lay exactly where he'd placed her. Her long blonde hair rested in silver swirls as if positioned by a photographer.

He heard it then, the noise that must have woke him. At first it seemed like someone beating on the floor, just pounding on the floor. Then the noise became familiar. It was a tumble dryer, thumping out a heartbeat. Poor Donald, poor old Donald. He was up late drying his clothes, and with each turn and thump they were losing the scents that had built up and clung on. Ethel's sweet perfume from where she'd rest her head by his collar... the aroma of her cooking, caked among the crevices. Dust, too, was slowly coming loose.

—— Lewis didn't sleep till morning crept into the room. He relished it and at the same time feared the day he might not relish it again. The songs of the birds seemed attached to the sunrise, stapled by their wings. Instead of counting sheep, he counted off the recently dead: one, two...

***

Double-Oh-Seven
Cameron Steel

————

You'll never have a Black Bond,
said the boy biting his
bourbon biscuit
and dipping it
in his tea
with a –
of
milk

(he was not a savage)

Mother
Cameron Steel

————

The moon shone like a newborn
son, where his mother's hopes lay
wondering in the treacle night
what would come with the dripping sand
where the tide licked and lapped
at his cold dead toes like a
childhood pet.

Shadows

Cameron Steel

———

In the daytime, in the corners
cracks and paper bags the
ragged edges of tatty-jeaned memories
frayed. I'm afraid

You have a shadow,
I have a shadow,
mine's behind me
yours on your lung

In the night, in the branches
that claw and cackle with dirty
fingerprints on my ceiling,
the trees cough

You have a shadow,
I have a shadow
mine's behind me
yours on your lung.

The Colour Red

Kathy Kunz

Tuesday

Dear Oma,

Today I wear my hair up, like you always ask me to. It feels different. The curls are so tightly pinned I fear for my scalp. I have already chipped the expensive pearl nail varnish. But you don't like me wearing red, you say it is the colour suited to a *Strassendirne*. I look like I am going to a wedding. Wilting mustard-coloured gerbera tucked behind my ear and all.

Even Michael has come. He said, 'I didn't recognise you.' He wouldn't. I haven't run around his back yard chasing geese for a long time now. He said, 'If only I was twenty years younger…' I know, Michael. If you were, I bet you would have proposed, wife, children, geese or not. I dare say you would approve, Oma.

I have put Teddy in a blanket, in a box and wrapped the box with a thousand threads. He is coming with you, but I don't want him to get cold or get lost on the way. I managed to read you one of Gibran's sweetest poems. I hope you understood it. I couldn't seem to get the words out right and only now realise it was in English. Does it even matter? Or is it all *Musik* to your ears anyway?

Thursday

Dear Oma,

The flowers I brought you haven't even wilted yet. It was supposed to be a Happy Bouquet. Submarine-yellow roses. Palest ochre Irises. No lilies.

I held your thrashing hands. I wet your dry mouth. And still the cogs of the clockwork ruptured. In my own head it sounded like I was drowning behind those grey blinds that they were closing on your windows – as if they were trying to contain us, like animals, dare I disturb the silent Britishness around us.

They gave me your earrings. I put them in my lobes. They were still warm. Lisann took my hand. And held it all the way as we walked through the artificial pools of dirty orange light back to our big Premier Inn double bed. We lay till morning, and she didn't let go.

Wednesday

Dear Oma,

You weren't in the big, shared room today. I ran and ran and ran. And still couldn't find you. A girl in her blue uniform brought me to you. You are in a room of your own now. It has a big plastic red hexagon on the door and the traffic light sign by your bed has gone from amber to crimson. You don't like red.

Lisann sits with me, in this darkened room with a view onto the concrete car park lot and we watch the tubes go into you and a horrible dark liquid drip into a sack from somewhere around your middle. If you saw what you were wearing now, you'd be mortified.

I have left Teddy with you. I remember how we used to play *Rommé* and I wish you would wake up and we could do that now. Instead, I continue reading to you. You are reading *Fortuna's Tochter* and we are now at chapter thirty. I just wish you could nod, blink, smile. You hate to leave books unfinished. Can you hear me, Oma? Can you hear me?

Monday

Dear Oma,

One train, one car and five hours later I parked Daddy's Merc like a blind person, almost brought you some fresh road kill instead of this big bouquet. But you smile and call me your *Engel* and I forget to worry about points and parking penalties. I get embarrassed, and shed a tear. You start to tell me what the flowers mean. Apparently, I have brought you symbols of wisdom and friendship.

I tell them they need to speak slowly with you. And I tell you what they tell me – you fell. Our Postie found you and brought you here. You've ruined our new white cushions, which he put under your head, with big red dollops. Funnily, it just looks like a messy child has spilt sauce. Do you remember when I was little you would take me out onto your back terrace and we would sit together in the warm Berlin summer sun? You used to put flowery cushions onto the wooden bench so my bottom didn't get cold. Then you'd bring out your collection of leather boxes. You'd place them in front of me and my heart would beat so fast, like that of our sparrow friend which always sat expectantly on your kitchen windowsill. For a few hours, the magpie-child could drape herself in glowing saffron-coloured gold, ivory pearls and sunset-orange amber and admire herself in your cloudy-sky coloured eyes. I would feel like a queen – extending my arms to admire the bracelets that could've fit around my thighs swinging in the golden light whilst rubies and tiny diamond splinters like microscopic shards of the rainbow twinkled on my pudgy fingers. You know exactly how to keep me quiet. Sometimes, you would let me leave them on for lunch. And then, of course, I would spill some sweet substance – maybe *Schokopudding* or *Malzbier* – all down my adorned front and the *Juwelen Prinzessin* turned into a guilty-looking little girl once again.

Why did you fall? You can't seem to remember. It doesn't matter. I'm here now.

The Colour Red by Kathy Kunz

Plattenbauten

Martin Schauss

———

We took a stroll
through the suburbs to count
the windows.
The windows it would take us
to find our way. To
recognise our parents
among the millions.

First Confession

Craig Lamont

—— Her hands pressed red buttons through holes at the neck of her cotton blouse. There was a kind of confirmation in each closing up, each shift from one button to the next, her fingers stiff and thin as church candles. In her wake he never slept, sins were bright and flickering and long overdue to be forgotten.

Thank you.

*The contributors to **Valve Journal** would like to thank:*

―――

John Hogg
Maureen Noor
Doug Johnstone
Alasdair Braidwood
Bryony Stocker
Adrian Searle
Mark Buckland
Rodge Glass
Liz Finnegan
Matrix Management Consultancy
Louise Welsh
Alan Bissett
Dilys Rose
University of Strathclyde Mature Students Association
University of Strathclydes Students Association
School of Humanities, University of Strathclyde
Journalism and Creative Writing, University of Strathclyde
Natalia Rose
Michael Clarkson